A Cost-Effectiveness Study of Clinical Methods of Birth Control: With Special Reference to Puerto Rico

William John Kelly

The Praeger Special Studies program—utilizing the most modern and efficient book production techniques and a selective worldwide distribution network—makes available to the academic, government, and business communities significant, timely research in U.S. and international economic, social, and political development.

A Cost-Effectiveness Study of Clinical Methods of Birth Control: With Special Reference to Puerto Rico

Praeger Publishers   New York   Washington   London

PRAEGER SPECIAL STUDIES IN INTERNATIONAL ECONOMICS AND DEVELOPMENT

PRAEGER PUBLISHERS
111 Fourth Avenue, New York, N.Y. 10003, U.S.A.
5, Cromwell Place, London S.W.7, England

Published in the United States of America in 1972
by Praeger Publishers, Inc.

© 1971 by William J. Kelly

Library of Congress Catalog Card Number: 72-79559

Printed in the United States of America

ACKNOWLEDGMENTS

I wish to thank the members of my dissertation committee—Professors Donald Huddle, Stanley Besen, and Robert Dix of Rice University—for their many hours of assistance and for their encouragement of this research project. I owe a special debt to Dean Ferdinand K. Levy and to my former classmates Karen Davis and Dagoberto Brito, all of whom had a significant effect on the basic methodology of the study. In addition, I have profited from many helpful comments by Professors Richard Young and Charles McLure of Rice University and Professors William Barnes, Harold Cohen, Edward Meeker, William Miller, and Paul Rubin of the University of Georgia. I owe an incalculable debt to Antonio Hernandez Torres, M.D., of the Medical School of the University of Puerto Rico for providing the empirical data used in this study. My data gathering was made easier by Adaline P. Satterthwaite, M.D., whom I have never met but whose superb records have won my respect. Financial support was provided by the Advanced Research Projects Agency of the Department of Defense through the Center for Research in Social Change and Economic Development at Rice University under contract N00014-67-A-0145-0001. Refinements of the original manuscript were made possible by summer research support provided by the University of Georgia during the summer of 1971. Finally, I wish to thank my wife and family for their years of patience and understanding; my mother for typing the final manuscript; and the editors of Demography and Studies in Family Planning for permitting the use of materials that appeared in articles of mine in those journals.

554092

CONTENTS

LIST OF TABLES

ix

INTRODUCTION

During its 1968-69 fiscal year, India budgeted 370 million rupees ($51.1 million) for government family planning programs, and by the 1973-74 fiscal year it plans to be spending 750 million rupees ($103.5 million) per year for such programs.[1] Over 23 developing countries at present have official government birth control programs and in 22 others private programs are under way, often with indirect government participation.[2]

Current evidence on the costs and benefits of birth control suggests that such expenditures are justified. Stephen Enke has concluded that "if economic resources of given value were devoted to retarding population growth, rather than accelerating production growth, the former resources could be 100 or so times more effective in raising per capita incomes in many L.D.C.'s."[3]

Formulation of a rational public expenditure policy in the area of family planning requires more than just a rough comparison of costs and benefits. Efficient allocation under such a program requires: first, evidence that government intervention is justified; second, expansion of the program to the point where the marginal benefits of the program equal the marginal costs of the program; and third, allocation of funds within the program so that the marginal costs of preventing births with different combinations of methods and users are equated.

A convincing case can be made for public birth control expenditures using the externalities argument. Birth control is said to lead to community benefits such as a reduction in abortions, illegitimate births, and unconscious infanticide; a reduction in poverty and the social ills that poverty creates; avoidance of crowding; greater investment and faster growth as a result of higher family and government saving; and avoidance of famine.[4] Since such benefits are largely external benefits which are nonappropriable, they tend to be underprovided by private market mechanisms. Hence, there is an argument for the government to intervene and improve resource allocation by taxing the beneficiaries and using the proceeds to expand production of birth control services.*

---

*Arguments for public birth control are often stated in distributive terms, as well as allocative terms. Society feels an obligation

Expansion of birth control programs to an optimum size, i.e., to the point where marginal social costs equal marginal social benefits, requires estimates of the costs and benefits of birth control. As indicated above, there is evidence, at present levels of production of birth control services, that the benefits of these services are very large relative both to the costs of the services and to the benefits of other programs with similar budgets.

The present study is directed at the third aspect of efficient public birth control—allocation of funds among alternative combinations of methods and users. Whether birth control programs are of optimum or suboptimum size it is desirable to be able to compare the costs of preventing births with different combinations of methods and users, and at different levels of output, so that the number of births prevented, and hence the benefits of birth control, may be maximized with whatever budget is available. In order to determine the cost of preventing births under these differing circumstances, the study must not only examine the economic phenomena behind provision of birth control services, but must also take account of psychological, sociological, and physiological factors that influence the acceptability and effectiveness of birth control methods (and hence the number of births prevented) in various socioeconomic settings. This has not yet been done adequately in a single study, as will be evident from Chapter 1.

The study is divided into two parts. The first part, consisting of Chapters 1-3, focuses on methodological problems of evaluating the costs and effectiveness of various birth control methods, drawing together existing theory on this subject and developing new theory. The second part, consisting of Chapters 4-6, is an empirical examination of the costs and effectiveness of various birth control methods in use in Puerto Rico. The study reviews the economic and demographic situation in Puerto Rico, provides estimates of the costs of preventing birth with the principal combinations of methods and patients in use at present in Puerto Rico, and discusses some improvements that might be made in these programs.

The study is limited to clinical programs and does not consider commercial programs. Clinical programs rely heavily upon direct

---

to transfer part of its resources from prosperous groups to the domestic and foreign poor. At the same time there is a feeling, particularly among the prosperous, that such transfers should be reduced, limited, or at least allowed to grow only at a controlled rate. Government birth control programs are seen as a means of limiting the size of, or rate of growth of, these needy groups and hence the amount of the transfer.

contact between contraceptive users and trained family planning personnel and are characterized by such activities as medical examination of prospective contraceptive users, formal assistance in the choice and use of methods, and follow-up activities. By contrast, commercial programs rely on indirect contact between contraceptive users and family planning workers through intermediate agents such as advertising media and retail establishments and do not involve medical examinations or other direct attempts to match users with methods.

The study was limited to clinical approaches because they are more common, there are more data on them, and they are easier to evaluate.

A final characteristic of the study is that it treats birth control largely in an economic development context. While public birth control is an important tool in combating poverty and other social problems in advanced countries, the author feels that it is most important for developing countries and has therefore chosen that context. The analysis is general enough, however, to be applied in other contexts.

INTRODUCTION NOTES

1. "India: A Bleak Demographic Future," Population Bulletin, XXVI, 5 (November 1970), 6.

2. Luther J. Carter, "Population Control: U.S. Aid Program Leaps Forward," Science, CLIX (February 9, 1968), 611-14.

3. Stephen Enke, "The Economic Aspects of Slowing Population Growth," The Economic Journal, LXXVI, 30 (March 1966), 56. Additional references to studies of the value of preventing births are presented in the Bibliography.

4. Further comments on individual, family and community benefits, together with supporting references, are presented in Chapter 1.

The purposes of this chapter are first, to explain why, in this study, cost per birth prevented is the proper criterion of success in providing family planning services; second, to review the literature dealing with calculation of the cost of preventing births; and third, to explain how this study represents an improvement over previous cost-effectiveness studies of family planning programs.* The literature dealing with specialized aspects of provision of contraceptive services and estimation of fertility reduction will be integrated into the specialized chapters that follow. This chapter is therefore limited to consideration of general approaches to calculation of the cost of preventing births.

THE CRITERION PROBLEM

Before embarking on a journey, it is advisable for a traveler to ask himself where he is going, why he is going, and how he will know when he has arrived. It would seem advisable for governments to ask similar questions before embarking on social programs aimed at promoting the general welfare. In the present context the relevant questions are the following: What is the objective of a family planning program, why is this objective desirable, and how can one measure the efficiency of a particular program in fulfilling this objective?

The answers to the first two questions are deceptively easy: the logical ultimate objective of any public expenditure program

----

*Chapter 6 points out some of the ways in which this study was not able to improve on previous studies.

should be to maximize the net contribution of the program to social welfare, i.e., to maximize the excess of utility produced by the program over utility sacrificed in carrying out the program. Advocates of family planning programs argue that such programs produce certain benefits and that the utility produced by these benefits exceeds the utility consumed in providing the contraceptive services.

Family planning programs are expected to produce (a) individual benefits such as better physical and mental health for mothers, lessened anxiety for breadwinners, and greater parental attention for children; (b) family benefits such as the ability to limit the total number of children born to the family so that per capita income and wealth within the family is increased, or the ability to control the spacing of births is increased so that child-related expenditures can be timed to fall within convenient periods in the family's life cycle of income; and (c) community, national, and international benefits such as reduction of the incidence of abortion, illegitimate birth, and unconscious infanticide;[1] a reduction in poverty and the social ills that poverty creates;[2] avoidance of crowding; greater investment and faster growth as a result of higher family and government saving;[3] avoidance of famine; maintenance of export capacity;[4] and protection of the environment.

Assuming that family planning programs do produce desirable benefits, one is still left with the problem of measuring the efficiency of a particular program in producing these benefits—i.e., the problem of selecting a "success criterion." What is needed is a quantifiable index of benefits or costs per unit of output of the program.

Since benefits and costs cannot be measured directly in terms of utility, it is commonly agreed that they should be converted into dollar values. For lack of a better measure, the numerator of the success criterion can therefore be thought of as costs or benefits, expressed in dollars.

There is much less agreement on what the relevant output denominator is. W. Parker Mauldin argues that the really important measure is "the extent to which individual families have been able to plan the timing and number of their births."[5] This suggests that output should be measured in terms of number of families helped.

Shri D. P. Karmarkar, the former Union Minister of Health for India, has said of India's program that the "double objective of the family planning program was to carry the family planning message into every home and to make family planning advice available in every hospital and dispensary."[6] This suggests that output should be measured in terms of service outlets or informed families.

In a recent cost-effectiveness study, David Seidman recommends separate analysis of each stage in the provision of family planning services and advocates the use of a variety of criteria such as cost per registrant, proportion of the population reached, cost per appointment kept, the continuation rate, the pregnancy rate, and cost per recipient.[7]

Obviously, there are plenty of candidates for the output denominator of the success criterion. But which is really relevant?

Given the fact that the ultimate output, utility, is unmeasurable and elusive, it would be desirable to use an output measure that is closely associated with the utility-producing benefits but which is also quantifiable and controllable. Close association is desirable to ensure confidence in obtaining a reasonable measure of the quantity of benefits that are being produced. And from a practical point of view, it is desirable to have a measure that can be calculated and can serve as a control variable.

If these characteristics are accepted, then the logical output measure is the number of births prevented. Other indexes such as the number of intrauterine devices (IUDs) inserted, cycles of pills distributed, workers trained, etc. may aid in efficient administration of a program but they cannot really serve as criteria of program success because they are only intermediate products of the program. The ultimate purpose of a family planning program is not to distribute contraceptives, spend funds, or train workers. It is to prevent births and thereby create certain benefits for families and society. The ultimate criteria should therefore be stated as the cost per birth prevented and the benefits per birth prevented, measured in dollars.

The present study does not deal with the benefits of family planning, but rather seeks to focus on the problem of calculating the cost of preventing births under various circumstances.* While specialization on the cost-effectiveness problem is reasonable given the magnitude of the job and the amount of research that has already been done on benefit problems, the reader should remember that this is only half the picture and that efficient allocation of family planning funds requires data on both costs and benefits.

If attention is to be focused on the cost side of the picture, then the relevant criterion will be the cost per birth prevented. But what costs?

Rational economic calculation is generally concerned with marginal measures—marginal cost, revenue, or utility. Ideally, it is best to be able to compare the marginal utility of an extra birth prevented with the marginal disutility of an extra birth prevented. Given the impossibility of this and the limitations of the present study, the next best measure

----

*The interested reader will find a number of references dealing with the benefits of family planning in the Bibliography.

is the marginal cost of a birth prevented at different rates of output and under different demographic circumstances.

It is also important to specify the time framework of costs. Family planning expenditures made today may prevent births over several years and may entail costs (e.g., side effects) over an equal or longer period of time. Some means must be found for comparing intertemporal streams of costs and births prevented.

Economists generally assume that a dollar today is worth more than a dollar n years in the future because today's dollar can be invested now at some interest rate r and will have grown to $(1 + r)^n$ dollars after n years. Conversely, a dollar n years from now is worth only $\frac{1}{(1 + r)^n}$ dollars today. Thus, a simple way to compare intertemporal cost streams is simply to reduce them all to present discounted values. This has been recognized in some studies of contraceptive costs.[8]

The problem of comparing a birth prevented today with a birth prevented tomorrow has generally been ignored except when discussed in a full cost-benefit context.[9] Since the present study measures benefits only in terms of the number of births prevented, this approach cannot be used. The best approach is to employ a discounting procedure to convert births prevented tomorrow into an equivalent number of births prevented today.[10] The reasoning follows.

Suppose actions taken today (year $\underline{O}$) will avert $\underline{A}$ births in year $\underline{n}$. If the value, in year $\underline{n}$, of a birth prevented is V_p dollars, then the value in that year of the benefits accruing from today's action is:

$$TB_n = \overline{A} \cdot V_{\underline{p}}. \tag{1-1}$$

If the discount rate is $\underline{r}$, then the present value of $A.V_p$ dollars is:

$$TB_O = \frac{A\,V_p}{(1 + r)n} = A\,\frac{\cdot V_p}{(1 + r)n} = \frac{A}{(1 + r)n} \cdot V_p. \tag{1-2}$$

All three formulations amount to the same thing, but the last form has special advantages in the present study.

With this formulation total cost functions can be estimated having the form:

$$TC = f\left[\frac{A}{(1 + r)^n}\right]. \tag{1-3}$$

Assuming that V_p does not vary between groups covered by the same programs,* future researchers can supply total benefit functions of the form:

$$TB_o = V_p \left[\frac{A}{(1 + r)n} \right] , \tag{1-4}$$

and, with this plus the total cost function, can estimate the optimum scale of the program.

CALCULATION OF THE COST PER BIRTH PREVENTED

A number of studies of contraceptive programs have included calculations of the cost of preventing a birth, but almost all of them are incomprehensive rule-of-thumb calculations which cover only a fraction of the multitude of possible production situations.

Robert Repetto's study of the Madras vasectomy program (see footnote 9) never states the cost per birth prevented, but the average cost for the program as a whole can be calculated from Repetto's figures if one is willing to discount future streams of births prevented and divide this into the program costs.[11] Repetto's cost estimates are based on centrally-sanctioned staffing patterns and do not include

---

*This is a common, convenient, and somewhat misleading assumption. Some benefits, such as reduction of maternal mortality rates must vary across age groups since older women have a higher ratio of deaths to births than do younger women. Thus it may be worth more to prevent a birth by an older woman than by a younger one, ceteris paribus. For evidence on the relationship between age and the ratio of maternal deaths to live births, see N. J. Eastman and L. M. Hellman, Williams' Obstetrics (13th ed.; New York: Appleton-Century-Crofts, 1966), p. 5.

A problem could also arise if V_p were expected to vary substantially over time. In that event, this approach would be inappropriate. The present writer doubts that the field will be sophisticated enough to project future levels of V_p for many years, however, and therefore does not consider this possibility to be a serious obstacle to the present study. See also Chapter 6.

costs of buildings, furnishings, or certain forms of overhead. The author does not offer his figures as the most accurate estimates, but rather as upper limits. A notable feature of his study is his attempt to estimate the cost of eliminating certain side effects of the program, something which most studies ignore.[12]

Stephen Enke's article (see footnote 3, Introduction) compares costs for a wide range of methods but his figures on cost per user are rough estimates for underdeveloped areas in general rather than specific countries. Notable features of his study are (a) his discussion of the difference between expenditures that represent resource costs and those that are only transfer payments, and (b) his calculation of the value of postponing a birth. Enke estimates that cost-effectiveness ratios may differ by a factor of as much as 250 between methods.[13]

S. M. Keeny et al. estimate the average cost of preventing a birth using the IUD in Korea.[14] They estimate that it cost about $1.5 million to insert 305,359 loops or about $4.91 per loop. Assuming that each loop prevents 0.64 births, they calculate the cost per birth averted at $7.66.[15]

B. M. Mahajan (see footnote 8, this chapter) calculates the average cost per birth prevented in India using IUDs and vasectomies by dividing program costs by the estimated number of births prevented.[16] Applying a 7 percent discount rate to costs, he estimates the cost per birth prevented at 32 rupees for vasectomies and 34 rupees for the IUD.[17]

The most detailed treatment of the cost per birth prevented is that of George Zaidan.[18] Zaidan estimates the cost of preventing births in Egypt using pills and the IUD. The heart of his procedure is the formula:

$$\frac{\text{Total Cost}}{\text{Total Births Prevented}} = \frac{V_1 \sum_{i=1}^{n} \sum_{t=1}^{T} x_{it} + V_2 \left(\sum_{i=1}^{n} u_i x_{i1} + \frac{1}{2} \sum_{t=2}^{T} u_1 x_{1t} \right) + FC}{(1-r) \sum_{t=1}^{T} \sum_{i=1}^{N} M_i x_{it}} \qquad (1-5)$$

where

FC = fixed costs;

V_1 = time-dependent cost per unit of time per acceptor;

V_2 = initial costs per acceptor;

m_i = "foregone" fertility of the ith age group, per unit of time;

x_{it} = total acceptors in the ith age group in time interval t (i=1, n; t=1, T where T = the length of the time horizon);

$u_i = \dfrac{T}{L_i}$ where L_i is the length of time over which initial costs are assumed to have their effect; and

r_i = the percent of acceptors who do not make effective use of contraceptives per unit of time.[19]

While this procedure is basically the same as that of Mahajan in that total program costs are divided by total births prevented, Zaidan's approach is preferable because it permits prediction of costs and because it takes account of individual cost components such as fixed costs, initial costs, and time-dependent costs. In addition, this formula could be used to calculate the cost per birth prevented for different program sizes or methods, or for classes of users who differ in age, cultural background, or even length of time in the program.

Zaidan does not choose to take advantage of these options, limiting his calculations instead to the costs of all-IUD or all-pill programs in rural or urban areas and serving 600,000 people having known demographic characteristics. Costs for programs employing different mixes of IUDs and pills and different mixes of rural and urban patients are then prepared using weighted averages of the costs of specialized programs.

Noteworthy features of Zaidan's study are his attempt to calculate the cost of preventing births by investment in primary and secondary education and his estimation of the number of potential acceptors from surveys of desired and actual family sizes.

John A. Ross has made a most valuable compilation of cost statistics from various programs around the world.[20] Ross includes estimates of costs per unit of service as well as per birth prevented. Of particular interest were figures from Chicago Planned Parenthood which calculated contraceptive costs on the basis of the number of service visits per year. Patients were expected to visit the clinic four times per year at a cost of $10 per visit or $40 per year. Assuming 4,200 patients per year and 3,360 prevented births yields a cost per birth prevented of $50.[21]

A study by David R. Seidman (see footnote 7, this chapter) is of interest because of its methodological insights rather than its results. It is not an integrated discussion of the problem of calculating the cost of preventing births, but is rather a survey of, and commentary on, different methods of recruiting, retaining, and serving patients.[22] Seidman's study is methodologically superior to the others because of its recognition of the need to employ production functions, marginal cost data, detailed demographic data, and information on side effects. Notable features of his study are his separate estimates and summaries of the costs of recruiting, serving, and retaining patients by various means.[23] Its chief fault is that it does not draw its various insights together into a single method for calculating the cost of preventing births.

CRITICISMS AND
PROPOSED IMPROVEMENTS

The present study is an improvement on previous attempts to calculate the cost of preventing births because, in general: (1) it estimates costs for real situations rather than hypothetical ones, (2) costs are estimated from production functions rather than from raw cost data, (3) it focuses on marginal costs rather than average costs, (4) it disaggregates costs to take account of a variety of method-user situations, (5) it relies on detailed local demographic data in estimating the number of births prevented, (6) it takes account of the intertemporal nature of costs and outputs through discounting, and (7) it recognizes the resource cost of contraceptive side effects. While some previous studies have taken account of each of the above factors, this is the only study to date that has taken account of all of these factors, or even a majority of them. It remains to explain the importance of each of these points and to show how the present study will improve on previous ones in each of these respects.

The first characteristic of this study is that wherever possible it seeks to calculate the cost of preventing births under real rather than hypothetical circumstances. Hypothetical calculations such as those which Enke has made are useful in showing the great excess of contraceptive benefits over contraceptive costs, but are of little help to clinic managers in allocating funds among different combinations of methods and users. It is not possible to make statements about the absolute or relative cost-effectiveness of different birth control methods that will hold true in widely separated locations because of local differences in factor costs and productivities and differences in demographic variables. It is a major theme of this study that allocation of birth control funds cannot be carried out adequately without calculations of the cost of preventing birth based on local cost and demographic data. The author seeks to demonstrate the need for such local calculations and to provide a general method that will make local calculation feasible.

A second characteristic of this study is that costs are estimated from production functions rather than from simple data on program costs and output. Of all the previous writers on this subject only Seidman has indicated a clear understanding of the need for estimating production functions first and then costs:

> Ideally, a set of experiments should be made which enable us to construct a "production function" that shows possible mixes of skills to service one patient's visit. . . . By determining this production function for the patient visit,

we could then establish which mix of manpower is the
least costly per patient visit.[24]

The other writers have either missed this point entirely or, at
best, have stumbled against it only accidentally.[25] It is easy to see
the advantage of estimating costs from production functions rather
than from direct cost data. What does it profit an administrator in
Bombay to know the cost of preventing a birth in an isolated village
if he knows very well that the prices of the productive factors are
different in the city from those in the village? And of what use will
today's cost figures be to the village administrator after his factor
prices change? But if each of them knew the production function
relating contraceptive outputs to capital and labor inputs they might
be able to supply current local input prices and calculate the cost in
their particular time-place situations.

A third characteristic of this study is that it focuses on marginal
costs rather than average costs. A typical approach in the literature
is to derive the average cost per birth prevented for a whole program
by dividing the total cost of the program by the estimated total number
of births prevented.[26] A rare exception to this pattern is the Seidman
study.[27] Average cost information may help an administrator to know
if his program is making a net contribution to social welfare (assuming
he has data on the benefits of a birth prevented) and may allow him to
compare the costs of his program with those of other programs, but
without information on the marginal cost of preventing a birth he
cannot hope to expand his program to optimal size. Concentration on
average costs can be partially justified if marginal cost is expected
to remain constant in the relevant output range since average cost
will then either equal marginal cost, or, at worst, approach it
asymptotically. However, it can only be an approximation to marginal
costs.

A fourth feature of this study is that it derives cost figures for
a variety of method-user circumstances and provides a method
whereby costs can be estimated for still other circumstances. Many
of the studies cited above calculate separate costs for different methods
and some, such as Zaidan's, calculate the costs for rural and urban
groups. But most studies ignore the fact that the nature of the productive process and the demographic characteristics of the patients
may cause the cost of preventing a birth to vary with the size of the
program, socioeconomic characteristics of the patient, age, or the
length of time that the patient has been in the program.

A fifth characteristic is that it relies on detailed local demographic data in estimating the number of births prevented. As will
be shown in Chapter 3, accurate estimation of the number of births
prevented requires a number of pieces of demographic information

such as parity rates, continuation rates, accidental pregnancy rates, etc. While some writers such as Zaidan show an awareness of the complexity of the demographic side of the problem, others such as Keeny are content to rely on rules of thumb such as "each loop prevents 0.64 births."

A sixth feature of this study is that it takes account of the intertemporal nature of costs and outputs through discounting. As noted in the discussion of the criterion problem, society does not place an equal value on resources today and resources tomorrow nor on benefits today and benefits tomorrow. In spite of this commonly recognized fact, only Mahajan has made any attempt to apply discounting to the problem of calculating the cost of preventing birth.

Finally, this study recognizes the resource cost of side effects. It is well known that the leading contraceptives have a variety of side effects which range from minor annoyances such as nausea to increased incidence of death from thromboembolic diseases.* It is also known that cost-benefit studies should take account of such side effects.[28] Yet only Seidman and Repetto comment on these and only the latter attempts to estimate the cost of correcting these side effects.

SUMMARY

It is evident that the proper success criteria to apply in evaluating family planning programs are the costs and benefits, measured in dollars, per birth prevented. A review of the literature reveals that there were numerous shortcomings in previous attempts to estimate the cost of preventing births. The present study will seek to correct these failings by drawing together what is best in the literature and welding it into a unified and general method for estimating the cost of preventing births. This improved method will then be applied to a family planning program in Puerto Rico. Finally, recommendations will be made for further research and for improvements in the operation of family planning programs.

---

*The Appendix contains a discussion of these problems.

2

In order to determine the cost per birth averted for a given method-patient combination one must estimate the cost of supplying service to this patient for a given length of time (e.g., one year) and then estimate the number of births averted during that period. This chapter will focus on the first part of the problem, taking up the production and cost concepts needed to calculate the cost of supplying services. Chapter 3 will examine the demographic concepts needed to estimate the number of births averted by these services.

PLANNING EFFICIENT PRODUCTION

The single most important characteristic of the production process for contraceptive services is that it is a queuing phenomenon inasmuch as the quantity of output on any given day cannot be predicted exactly (except in the trivial case where a zero output is desired).* This is because the number of patients who come for contraceptive services on any particular day is a function of a multitude of stochastic events such as births, weather, travel conditions, and availability of baby sitters. As a result, clinic managers cannot control, or even predict, with precision what level of output will be produced at a given clinic on a given day and hence cannot adjust clinic inputs to minimize the cost of that output or even ensure technically efficient production. Because of this fact, the traditional economic approach to production must be modified.

---

*The author is indebted to Dagoberto L. Brito for suggesting this conceptual framework.

A production function may be defined as an expression of the relationship between combinations of inputs and the corresponding maximum quantities of output obtainable with these inputs. Given enough observations of the appropriate type, such a production function could be estimated for family planning clinics. Without information on the probability distribution of patient arrivals, however, it would be of little help in planning efficient service production unless one or more of the following were true: (1) patients could be induced to appear at a particular time and place and in appropriate numbers, (2) the clinic would not hesitate to turn away patients when more come than can be handled with the planned inputs, (3) inputs could be shifted to other productive tasks when they were not needed to provide contraceptive services. These conditions generally do not obtain.

Family planning clinics have some control over the total number of patients who come and the timing of their visits, but the control is limited. The total number of patients is influenced by a variety of controllable factors such as advertising, patient charges, waiting time, and clinic location. The timing of visits may be controlled somewhat by the use of appointments and by dissemination of information on clinic hours. These devices may be used to raise the mean number of patients per clinic or to reduce the variance, but the variance cannot be completely eliminated and often remains great enough to hamper efficient production.

Clinics could also achieve greater productive efficiency and lower per unit costs by setting inputs at a low level and turning away excess patients. However, these patients might not return. Because there is evidence that the benefits of contraceptive services far outweigh the costs of providing them, there is a strong bias against such a course.

Finally, inputs that prove to be in excess can, under some circumstances, be put to other tasks and hence not go to waste. Full time clinic personnel often have patient records or other duties which can be attended to during slack periods. All of these techniques make it possible to put inputs on a flexible basis and hence to achieve greater productive efficiency.

The clinic manager should balance the costs of excess inputs against the benefits of extra births averted. If the benefits of birth control are believed to be high it should not be unusual to find excess inputs. This can be illustrated with a simple example.

Assume the existence of a single-clinic family planning organization serving a group of patients who are homogeneous in all important demographic respects (fertility, continuation rate, competence with birth control, etc.). This organization provides contraceptive service with a single method, utilizing $\underline{k}$ inputs to provide the service. Assume further that this service is provided through a process characterized by constant returns to scale and described by the production function:

$$X_c = f(Y_1, Y_2, \ldots\ldots\ldots\ldots Y_k) \qquad (2\text{-}1)$$

where

X_c = the output capacity of the clinic, that is, the maximum number of units of service that can be produced per unit of time, one unit of service providing a single patient with contraceptive protection for a known period of time; and

Y_i = the number of units of input i used per unit of time.

The clinic manager's control variable in maximizing net social benefits is X_c which he can control through adjusting the levels of the k inputs.

Given this production function and the per unit costs of these inputs, the clinic manager can derive a long-run total cost curve:

$$LRTC = f(X_c). \qquad (2\text{-}2)$$

On the benefit side, the clinic manager knows that total benefits are a function of the number of units of service dispensed or, equivalently, the number of patients served:

$$TB = f(X_s).* \qquad (2\text{-}3)$$

But since X_s cannot be known precisely beforehand, this relationship will be more operationally useful if it is restated in probabilistic terms as:

$$E(TB) = f[E(X_s)]. \qquad (2\text{-}4)$$

The expected number of patients served may in turn be expressed as:

$$E(X_s) = f[X_c, g(X_a)] \qquad (2\text{-}5)$$

---

*Units of service dispensed and patients served are numerically identical in the present example, by definition.

where

X_c = the clinic output capacity, as defined above; and

$g(X_a)$ = the density function of patient arrivals.

Assuming, for the moment, that $g(X_a)$ is a totally exogenous factor,* the expected benefit function may be rewritten as a function of X_c, the clinic manager's control variable:

$$E(TB) = f(X_c). \tag{2-6}$$

Given information such as:

V_p = the present value, in dollars, of a birth averted; and

B_a = the expected number of births averted per unit of service dispensed (patients served),

the clinic manager can define a total social benefit function:

$$E(TB) = V_p B_a \cdot E(X_s) \tag{2-7}$$

or, more precisely,

$$E(TB) = V_p B_a [\sum_{a=0}^{C} X_a g(X_a) + X_c \sum_{a=c+1}^{\infty} g(X_a)]. \tag{2-8}$$

With this cost and benefit information, the job of the clinic manager is to pick the level of X_c where

$$E(TB) - TC = \text{net social benefits} \tag{2-9}$$

is maximized.

Assuming constant returns to scale in the production of X_c and perfect competition in factor markets, the long-run total cost curve should be a linear increasing function of X_c. If there is a central

---

*If the willingness of patients to visit the clinic is affected by the expected waiting time or the probability of not being served at all, then $g(X_a)$ should be replaced with $g(X_a | X_c)$. This will be discussed further in Chapter 5.

tendency in $g(X_a)$ the total benefit function should increase as X_c increases, but beyond some point it should increase at a decreasing rate. If total benefits exceed total costs at some level of X_c, as is usually alleged, and if $g(X_a)$ approaches zero as X_a becomes very large, then there should be some clearly defined level of X_c at which net social benefits are maximized, and where marginal costs equal marginal social benefits, or in this case, where

$$MC = E(MB) = V_p B_a \sum_{a=c+1}^{\infty} g(X_a).* \qquad (2\text{-}10)$$

Given information on MC, V_p, B_a, and $g(X_a)$ the clinic manager can solve this equation for the optimum level of X_c.

In many cases a single-output approach to provision of con-traceptive services will not be adequate. First, most family planning programs do not offer contraceptive services with a single method, but instead follow a "cafeteria approach," offering patients a choice of several methods. Second, family planning clinics frequently offer noncontraceptive services such as postpartum examinations, cytology tests, and general gynecological services. Finally, even if a clinic does offer only a single method with no concomitant noncontraceptive services, there may be enough of a difference in the input requirements, for initial visits as opposed to follow-up visits and in the protection afforded by these visits, so that these visits must be treated as two distinct types of services. Under these circumstances the clinic manager is faced with the problem of planning for several types of service rather than a single type.

As long as production functions and cost functions can be defined

---

*The reasoning is:

$$E(MB) = \frac{\Delta E(TB)}{\Delta X_c} = V_p B_a \cdot \frac{\Delta E(X_s)}{X_{c+1} - X_c}$$

$$= V_p B_a [E(X_s)_{c+1} - E(X_s)_c]$$

$$= V_p B_a \sum_{a=c+1}^{\infty} g(X_a)$$

where $E(X_s)_{c+1}$ indicates the expected number of patients served when the clinic capacity is $c+1$.

in terms of individual outputs the existence of multiple services will offer no great problems and the above method of planning efficient production can be applied in slightly modified form. Where separate production and cost functions cannot be defined, the problem becomes more difficult, as will be seen in Chapter 5.

ESTIMATION OF THE PRODUCTION FUNCTION
FOR CONTRACEPTIVE SERVICES

The existence of queuing and multiple services in family planning clinics have a number of consequences for estimation of the production function for these services.

The stochastic nature of patient arrivals must make any given clinic appear to be operating frequently at less than capacity, even when production is planned in accordance with the previously mentioned principles for maximization of net benefits. That is, actual service levels of the clinic often will be less than the maximum levels implied by the production function and the given inputs of the clinic. An uncritical use of observations on such a clinic would obviously lead to underestimation of the production function.

This situation can be ameliorated by screening data on clinic inputs and outputs and deleting those observations that are dominated by other observations. Thus, if $X^{(1)}$ and $X^{(2)}$ are vectors of outputs secured from equal clinic inputs such that for every element x_i of the vectors

$$x_i^{(1)} \geq x_i^{(2)} \tag{2-11}$$

then $X^{(2)}$ is said to be dominated by $X^{(1)}$ and the observation containing $X^{(2)}$ should be discarded. Similarly, if output vector X has been produced by input vector $Y^{(1)}$ and by another input vector $Y^{(2)}$ and if for every element y_j of the vectors

$$y_j^{(1)} \leq y_j^{(2)} \tag{2-12}$$

then vector $Y^{(2)}$ is dominated by $Y^{(1)}$ and the observation containing $Y^{(2)}$ should be deleted.

One might also screen observations against linear combinations of other observations and delete any observations that are dominated by one of these linear combinations. This can be illustrated with a simple example. Consider a clinic that has a fixed amount of inputs

and is producing contraceptive services X_1 and X_2. The figure below
shows five output observations (A, B, C, D, and E) for such a clinic.
Since the clinic inputs are the same for all of these observations, it
is clear that $\underline{A}$ and $\underline{B}$ dominate $\underline{D}$ and $\underline{E}$, respectively. Neither $\underline{A}$ nor
$\underline{B}$ alone dominates $\underline{C}$. However, linear combinations of $\underline{A}$ and $\underline{B}$ may
be formed, having the general form

$$\lambda A + (1 - \lambda)\ B \qquad\qquad (2\text{-}13)$$

where $0 \leq \lambda \leq 1$. These linear combinations will lie along the line
segment joining points $\underline{A}$ and $\underline{B}$.[1] It is clear that a number of these
points will dominate $\underline{C}$.

This approach assumes, in effect, that if the clinic could produce
output combinations $\underline{A}$ and $\underline{B}$, then the clinic could have produced any
combination of X_1 and X_2 that lies along the line segment joining $\underline{A}$
and $\underline{B}$. It would do this by giving up some of one output and devoting
the freed resources to producing more of the other output.

There are several estimation problems which can arise because
of queuing and the screening process used to sort stochastic observations. First, the production function may be misestimated if the
production possibility curve is convex to the origin and linear combinations are used in screening the data. In this case, screening
observations against linear combinations of $\underline{A}$ and $\underline{B}$ might lead to an
estimated production possibility curve that overstates the capabilities
of the production function in certain regions. Second, if clinics tend
to be under capacity even when patient arrivals are at a relatively
high level, the capabilities of the production function will be under-
stated. Third, if under-capacity production occurs primarily in small
clinics (e.g., because of indivisibilities in factors) or primarily in
large clinics, the estimated production function will give an erroneous
indication of the extent of returns to scale.

Finally, the screening process by its very nature has a tendency

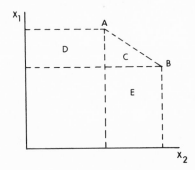

to increase the unadjusted and perhaps even the adjusted coefficients of determination. The more thorough the screening, the better the apparent fit of the estimated production function is likely to be. This is not, in itself, bad. If the form of the production function were properly specified, if no independent variables were omitted, and if there were no measurement errors in the data, then a high adjusted coefficient of determination would be a necessary condition for a good estimate of the production function. However, a high adjusted coefficient of determination is not a sufficient condition for a good estimate. The danger, then, is that screening may make a group of observations that lie well below the production frontier appear to be a well-defined part of the frontier itself.

There are several things that can be done to detect this problem, if not to ameliorate it. First, one may seek additional observations that dominate some or all of the observations in the screened data set. If such observations are found, then there is a danger of underestimation. Second, one may try to generate observations on a controlled basis, combining inputs and recording the maximum possible output. Thus, one might estimate the quantities of inputs required for each of the separate activities that comprise the production process, arrange these in a critical path map (CPM), and compare the input-output relationship implied by the CPM with that which has been estimated from the screened data. If the CPM relationship implies greater efficiency than is actually observed, then the empirical production function may be underestimated. Finally, one might try to detect underestimation by comparing the estimated production functions for two different types of outputs. If it is known that service S_1 requires more inputs per unit of output than service S_2, but the estimated production functions imply the reverse, then one or both of the production functions may be misestimated.

In the absence of independent evidence that either supports or contradicts the estimated production function, the problem of uncertainty will remain. In that event one must simply recognize the danger that the production function is underestimated or even that it shows an erroneous degree of returns to scale (if the degree of underestimation is greater among either small or large clinics) and mention these possibilities among the qualifications to the study.

It is evident that efficient production planning requires a number of pieces of information, most of which are of a local nature. The production function may or may not be specific to the locality, but the input costs, the present value of a birth averted, the expected number of births averted per unit of service dispensed, and the density function of patient arrivals are definitely of a local nature. As a result, efficient production planning must be based on information specific to the locality in question rather than data for other localities or for aggregations of localities.

The following chapter considers problems likely to be encountered in estimation of the demographic variables needed to calculate the number of births averted.

3

**DEMOGRAPHIC
CONCEPTS**

The purpose of the present chapter is to introduce the demographic concepts that are needed in this study. The first part of the
chapter will be devoted to an explanation of the mechanics of fertility
rates, contraceptive failure rates, and contraceptive continuation
rates. The second part will present four alternative ways of estimating
the number of births prevented with a given method/user combination.

FERTILITY, FAILURE, AND CONTINUATION RATES

Before proceeding to construct fertility rates, it will be useful
to define several terms that are used in this study.

The first of these, the age-specific fertility rate, or ASFR, is
the number of births to women of a certain age group during one year,
divided by the number of women in that age group. An age group may
be defined to include married women, unmarried women, or both. The
seven age groups which are commonly of interest are ages 15-19,
20-24, 25-29, 30-34, 35-39, 40-44, and 45-49.

The second term, fecundability, is defined as the probability
that a susceptible non-pregnant woman will conceive on a given day.
This is a modification of a definition used by Mindel C. Sheps and
Edward B. Perrin.[1]

Finally, a contraceptive method is defined as any means or
practice that serves to decrease fecundability.[2]

Age-Specific Fertility Rates

The number of births prevented by a contraceptive method is a function of the effectiveness of the contraceptive, the fertility of the user, and the continuation rate.* The number of births to married women of a given age group per year should equal the number of "woman-days available" during the 12 month period from 9 months before to 3 months after the beginning of the year in question times the probability of conception on each day times the ratio of live births to conceptions (B):

$$[\text{Births}]_{0 \text{ to } 12} = [\text{Prob. of conception/day}] \times [\text{woman-days avail.}]_{-9 \text{ to } +3} \times B \qquad (3\text{-}1)$$

The probability of conception per day under contraceptive conditions may be expressed as $Z_p \times \Sigma F$ where Z_p indicates fecundability and ΣF is the total probability of contraceptive failure. The term Z_p is a function of a number of factors such as the probability of intercourse on a given day, the probability of a woman being fertile on a given day, and the fertility of the male and female in question. Fecundability will therefore be influenced by anything that affects these factors including such things as age, frequency of separation of partners (e.g., military service, migration, or imprisonment), cultural habits, diet, and general state of health.

The number of woman-days available will equal the number of days in a year times the number of women available per day or:

$$\text{woman-days available} = 365 \, WA_v \qquad (3\text{-}2)$$

where

W = the number of women in the age group;

A_v = the percentage of women in the age group who are "available," i.e., not pregnant or lactating.**

---

*The following section is limited to derivation of fertility rates for married women, but could easily be modified for unmarried or mixed groups. For simplicity, it is assumed that patients drop from the program only if they become pregnant. Thus, the consideration of continuation rates is postponed until later in the chapter.

**There is ample evidence that lactation prolongs postpartum amenorrhea and hence provides a woman with some protection against

Substituting the foregoing terms into equation (3-1) and dividing by $\underline{W}$ gives the ASFR for this group:

$$ASFR = 365 \ Z_p \ \Sigma \ F \ B \ A_v \qquad (3-3)$$

The proportion of women who are "available" is a function of the probability of a fertile woman conceiving and the length of the period of pregnancy and subsequent nursing.

Assume that the probability of conception for an available woman on a given day is $N/1{,}000$. Thus, on day 1, $\underline{N}$ out of 1,000 available women will get pregnant and on day 2 there will be only 1,000-N available. But if this system is in a steady state equilibrium there will also be $\underline{N}$ returning from pregnancy on day 1 and thus 1,000-N+N or 1,000 will be available on day 2. If 1,000 are available on an average day and $\underline{N}$ leave the state each day while an equal number return after remaining out for $\underline{D}$ days, then $\underline{DN}$ members of the group are out of the state on the average and the total size of the group is 1,000 + DN. Therefore:

$$A_v = 1000/(1000 + DN). \qquad (3-4)$$

But since the probability of conception is known to be

$$N/1000 = Z_p \Sigma F$$

we can solve for $\underline{N}$ and substitute it into equation (3-4), obtaining

$$A_v = 1/(1 + DZ_p \Sigma F). \qquad (3-5)$$

Substituting A_v into equation (3-3) yields

$$ASFR = 365Z_p \ \Sigma FB/(1 + DZ_p \ \Sigma F), \qquad (3-6)$$

where

$$\frac{\partial \, ASFR}{\partial \, Z_p} > 0; \ \frac{\partial \, ASFR}{\partial \Sigma F} > 0; \ \frac{\partial \, ASFR}{\partial \, B} > 0$$

$$\frac{\partial \, ASFR}{\partial \, D} < 0.$$

---

pregnancy. See Christopher Tietze, "The Effect of Breast Feeding on the Rate of Conception," International Population Conference: New York, 1961, II (London, 1963), pp. 129-36.

It can be seen immediately that there will be a direct relation between ASFR and the parameter $\underline{B}$ since this term appears only in the numerator and has a straightforward multiplicative effect on ASFR. Similarly $\underline{D}$, which appears only in the denominator, will have a simple inverse effect on ASFR. The other two components bear a more complicated relation to ASFR as may be shown with a simple example.*

Assume that Z_p equals 1/60 or 0.0167. Assume also that B = 0.8 and, for the sake of simplicity, that this means that 8 live births result from every 10 conceptions, but that the miscarriages, etc. which eliminate the other 2 do not occur until the last of the $\underline{D}$ days. Finally assume that D = 270, and that no contraceptive of any type is being used so that $\Sigma F = 1$. Substituting these values into equation (3-6) gives an ASFR of 0.8852.

However, introducing a birth control method with a failure rate of $\Sigma F = 0.5$ (or a 50 percent effective method) reduces ASFR to only 0.7492 or by only about 15 percent. Similarly, introduction of a contraceptive with 90 percent effectiveness will reduce the initial ASFR by only about 62 percent. Other things equal, more births will be prevented by giving a 100 percent effective method to $\underline{x}$ percent of the population (where x < 100) than by giving an $\underline{x}$ percent effective method to 100 percent of the population. Only when the term $DZ_p \Sigma F$ in the denominator of equation (3-6) becomes relatively small (e.g., when ΣF is very low) does the ASFR decline in proportion to the decline in the failure rate.[†]

Contraceptive Failure Rates

The effectiveness of a contraceptive method may be defined as the "relative reduction in fecundability produced by its use."[3] If fecundability in the absence of contraception is Z_p^0 and with a given contraceptive method is Z_p^1, then the effectiveness of the method, expressed as a percentage, is $100 \left(1 - Z_p^1/Z_p^0\right)$.[4] This means that a method that reduces fecundability from 0.20 to 0.05 has an effectiveness

---

*The approach used here and the results are similar to those in Sheps and Perrin where computer simulations were used.

[†]It is evident from the form of equation (3-6) that experiments with Z_p will yield similar results.

of 75 percent. Conversely, the failure rate may be defined as Z_p^1/Z_p^0 or, in this case, 25 percent.

Effectiveness and failure rates vary among contraceptive methods and among groups of people because of differences in either the technological characteristics of the methods, or the behavioral and other characteristics of their users, or both. Because of these natural groupings, it is convenient to make a distinction between method failure rates and user failure rates.

Ideally a method failure rate would be a measure of the part of total observed failure that is inherent to, or attributable to, the method itself. An example of the technological characteristics behind method effectiveness might be the relative spermicidal action of a contraceptive jelly or cream.[5]

User failure, on the other hand, is related to physiological, behavioral, or other characteristics of the user. The rate of expulsion of IUDs is related to some extent to physiological characteristics which are influenced by age and parity;[6] individual success in contraception tends to increase as the desired family size is approached;[7] people in higher income groups tend to be more successful in contraception than do those in lower income groups using the same method;[8] apparently highly competent contraceptors may deliberately fail for complex psychological reasons.[9]

In practice it is impossible precisely to divide total failure into an amount attributable to the method and an amount attributable to the users. This is because the effectiveness of most methods cannot be ascertained except in active use and such active use necessarily introduces the human element and some degree of user failure.* Fortunately, reasonable approximations to user and method failure rates are possible and sufficient for most purposes. A useful approximation to the method failure rate is the minimum total failure rate that is observed for any distinct group of users such as well educated and highly motivated couples. The user failure rate is approximately equal to the difference between the total observed failure rate and the method failure rate. The total failure rate will, of course, be the sum of the method and user failure rates, minus the product of the two, assuming that they have independent probability distributions.

The second important distinction is between "use-related" failure and "installation-related" failure. Use-related failure refers to method or user failures that occur at the time of intercourse. Installation-

---

*For comments on the limited usefulness of pure laboratory evaluations of contraceptives, see J. MacLeod et al. (footnote 6, this chapter).

related failure refers to failures that occur some time before intercourse and leave the user unprotected when intercourse does occur.

A use-related failure rate therefore refers to the ratio of
unsuccessful uses of a method to the total number of uses, while an
installation-related failure rate is the ratio of faulty installations to
total installations. The first may be thought of as randomly distributed
instances of short-term vulnerability while the second will be mani-
fested in randomly distributed individuals who are unprotected for
extended periods of time.

Numerically similar use-related failure rates and installation-
related failure rates yield very different ASFRs and different numbers
of births prevented, as may be demonstrated with the above ASFR
formula. The ASFR formula for a method subject to use-related
failure is the same as that developed already:

$$ASFR = 365 \ Z_p \ \Sigma FB/(1 + DZ_p \Sigma F). \qquad (3-7)$$

Because such a contraceptive reduces the observed fecundability of
all women of a given group with an equal probability, its failure rate
should appear wherever Z_p appears. In short, the use-related failure
rate is simply ΣF.

By contrast, a method subject only to installation-related failure
divides the class of new users into two groups. One fraction, I_f, is
completely unprotected. The ASFR for this group is found by substituting 1 for ΣF in equation (3-7). The other fraction of users,
$(1-I_f)$, is completely protected. The ASFR for this group is found by
substituting 0 for ΣF in equation (3-7). The ASFR for the group as
a whole will be the weighted sum of the rates of the two subgroups:

$$ASFR = I_f \ x \ ASFR_{I_f} + (1 - I_f) \ x \ ASFR_{(1 - I_f)} \qquad (3-8)$$

$$= I_f \ x \ ASFR_{I_f} + 0$$

$$= I_f \ 365Z_p B/(1 + DZ_p). \qquad (3-9)$$

To illustrate the effect of these two types of failure on ASFR
and on the number of births prevented, consider a group of 2,000
women having the fertility parameters given in the above example.
The ASFR of the group in the absence of any form of birth control
(or $\Sigma F = 1$) is ASFR = 0.8852.

Assume that half of these women are given a method having a
use-related failure rate of 0.5. This amounts to substituting 0.5 into
equation (3-7) above and leads to ASFR = 0.7492.

The other 1,000 women are given a method having an installation-related failure rate of 0.5. The ASFR for this group will be the weighted average of the ASFR for a completely protected group (0.0000) and that for a completely unprotected group (0.8852) or

$$ASFR = 1/2 \ (0.0000) + 1/2 \ (0.8852)$$

$$= 0.4426$$

or lower than in the case of the method subject to a numerically equal use-related failure rate.

The number of births prevented in the first year by either method should equal

births prevented = (ASFR before - ASFR after) x W .   (3-10)

In the case of the 1,000 women using the method subject to use-related failure the number of births prevented will be 136.0 while in the case of the method subject to installation failure the number of births prevented will be 442.6. It is evident that a method with a given installation failure rate will prevent more births than a method with a numerically similar use-related failure rate, ceteris paribus.

The distinction between use-related failure and installation-related failure is important because the latter can be corrected partially by recycling the $\underline{Y}$ unsuccessful users through the clinic at the end of their pregnancies and converting them into $(1 - I_f) \ Y$ successful users and $I_f Y$ failures.* If the continuation rate is high, this recycling process can lead to an asymptotically decreasing failure rate for the total set of original acceptors as installation failures are detected and partially corrected. Such recycling is not effective with methods subject to use-related failure. This is because the total protection level for users of methods subject to use-failure is not a function of the number of installation cycles as it is with users of methods subject to installation failure.

---

*This assumes that installation failures are random events. This is often not the case—current data suggests that the rate of expulsion is two or three times as high for second installations as for first installations. See Mauldin et al. "Retention of IUD's," pp. 5-6.

Contraceptive Continuation Rates

The contraceptive continuation (or retention) rate, when expressed in mathematical form, indicates the percentage of initial contraceptive acceptors who will still be active a given number of months or years after accepting the method.

The continuation rate plays an important part in calculating the number of births averted inasmuch as all patients who accept birth control eventually discontinue it because they wish to have another pregnancy, they have become discontented with their contraceptive, or they are no longer in danger of conceiving (e.g., after menopause).

The continuation rate depends on a number of factors including the method, the age and race of the patient, and the length of time that the patient has been using the method.[10] In addition, continuation rates vary greatly from country to country. Oral contraceptive continuation rates after one year have ranged from 75.7 percent in one Ceylon program to 12.3 percent for a program in Turkey.[11] IUD continuation rates after one year (without reinsertions) have varied from 58.8 percent in one Korean program to 76.8 percent in Pakistan.[12] Therefore some estimate of the continuation rate must be made if a reasonable calculation of births averted is to be made.

Several researchers have concluded that, ceteris paribus, the continuation rate for either oral contraceptive or IUD users can be approximated by the general formula:

$$C = ae^{-rt} \tag{3-11}$$

where

C is the continuation rate at time t;

a is a constant indicating the percentage of patients who continue beyond their first visit (i.e., 1-a is the percentage who drop immediately);

e is the natural logarithm base;

r is the continuous rate of decline in the continuation rate; and

t is time expressed in years.[13]

This conclusion is not beyond challenge, however. M. -Françoise Hall and William A. Reinke found evidence that suggests that the rate of decline, r, is not constant but decreases as the time since acceptance increases.[14] In addition, there is little data on continuation rates beyond four or five years after acceptance. For these reasons, the decay form of the continuation rate should not be accepted blindly when calculating births averted but should instead be treated as a hypothesized form to be tested against other possible forms.

MEASUREMENT OF BIRTHS AVERTED

It is now possible to apply the concepts described above to the measurement of births averted.

The number of births averted per time period for a group of W women can be approximated by the formula:

$$\text{births averted} = (\text{ASFR}^0 - \text{ASFR}^1)\ W\ (C^0 + C^1)/2 \qquad (3\text{-}12)$$

where C stands for the contraceptive continuation rate, ASFR indicates the age-specific fertility rate for participants in the program, and the superscripts indicate values at the beginning of contraception (0) and at the end of the period in question (1).

There are four general ways of estimating the number of births prevented, depending on how one chooses to estimate the before and after ASFR and how wide a group is believed to be affected by the program. An indirect approach, which follows from the foregoing analysis, uses the known ASFR^0 and tries to deduce ASFR^1 from information on initial fertility rates and the failure rates of the method. The second set of approaches relies on direct measurements of both ASFR^0 and ASFR^1. The third method, which was developed by Robert Potter, focuses on the length of the interval between births rather than on ASFR.

The fourth and final method—the one used in this study—involves estimation of the number of births averted from parity data and information on the accidental pregnancy rate among users of the method. This method is simpler than the others and can be applied in a greater range of situations, but may not be as accurate.*

Indirect Estimation of Births Averted

Where direct measurements of fertility rates are not available, these may be estimated if sufficient information about the population and method is available.

---

*It would, of course, be difficult to establish the relative degrees of inaccuracy of the methods without applying all of the methods in the same situation. This is an area where more research is needed.

The change in fertility rates for age group i per time period (ignoring the discounting problem and continuation rates for the moment) using a particular method may be expressed as:

$$\Delta F_i = ASFR^0_{\mu i} - ASFR^1_{\mu i} \qquad (3\text{-}13)$$

where the 0 and 1 superscripts are as indicated above and the μ subscript indicates that the ASFR shown is that for age group i as a whole as opposed to subsets of this group.

If age group i is homogeneous with respect to native fertility and competence in the use of the new method, $ASFR^1_i$ should be uniform for all subsets of group i. However, this is not likely to be true of $ASFR^0_i$ since age group i may initially be composed of various subsets, some of which are already using birth control and others which are not. The initial rate may therefore be viewed as a weighted average of the fertility rates of these subsets.

Having assumed that group i is homogeneous with respect to native fertility, it is natural to postulate some base fertility rate $ASFR_b$, which would prevail among all subsets of group i in the absence of any form of birth control and which underlies the actual ASFR that are observed for each subset. The observed ASFR for the subset of group i which is using method j is a function of this base rate:

$$ASFR^0_{ij} = f_j(ASFR_b). \qquad (3\text{-}14)$$

Earlier it was shown that

$$ASFR = 365Z_p \, \Sigma FB/(1 + DZ_p \, \Sigma F) \qquad (3\text{-}15)$$

or

$$ASFR = 365 \, I_f Z_p B/(1 + DZ_p), \qquad (3\text{-}16)$$

depending on whether a method subject to use-related failure or installation-related failure is used. Hypothesizing the existence of a base fertility rate $ASFR_b$ that would prevail for all subgroups in age group i in the absence of all forms of birth control is equivalent to assuming that Z_p, B, and D are the same for all subsets of group i and that differences in the manifest fertility rates of the subsets, $f_j(ASFR_b)$, must be attributed to differences in the failure rates of the birth control methods used by the subsets.

It is evident from the preceding discussion that it should be possible to deduce the values of $ASFR^0_i$ and $ASFR^1_i$, and hence the change ΔF_i, when a new method is introduced, if the base rate $ASFR_b$ and enough of the parameters of equations (3-15) and (3-16) are known.

The base fertility rate $ASFR_b$ is easy to obtain since it is simply the fertility rate that is observed for any subgroup that is not practicing contraception (here labeled as subgroup 1). In terms of equation (3-15) this involves simply assuming that $\Sigma F = 1$ or

$$ASFR_b = f_1(ASFR_b) = 365\, Z_p B/(1 + DZ_p). \qquad (3-17)$$

From this base rate one may easily determine the fertility rate for a subgroup j that is using a contraceptive method subject to installation-related failure. Earlier it was shown that such a subgroup will be divided into two fractions I_{fj} and $1 - I_{fj}$, the first having no protection and the second having complete protection. Therefore, the ASFR equation for this group is the same as equation (3-16).*

If all contraceptive methods in use before and after initiation of the program were of this type, knowledge of $ASFR_b$ and the installation failure rate for each method would be sufficient to define the ASFR of each of the subgroups and hence ΔF_i.

Where methods subject to use-related failure are involved the problem is more complex. As indicated earlier, the failure rate ΣF for such methods modifies the Z_p term, which appears in both the numerator and denominator of the right side of equation (3-15). This equation cannot be solved even if both $ASFR_b$ and ΣF are available, unless some of the other parameters are known.

Assume that $ASFR_b$ is known. Equation (3-17) expresses the relationship between this quantity and Z_p, B, and D and can be solved for any one of these if the other two are known. More generally, equation (3-15) can be solved if any four of the five terms Z_p, ΣF, B, D, and ASFR are known. Unfortunately, the estimation of these parameters is often more difficult than direct measurement of the necessary ASFR.

Direct Estimation of Births Averted: The
Fertility Rate Approach

The second way of estimating the number of births averted is to measure directly the appropriate ASFR and to calculate the number of births averted via equation (3-12). W. Parker Mauldin distinguishes

---

*Equation (3-16) would have to be adjusted if failures were recycled.

three variations of this approach: (1) Comparison of actual births and expected births among participants based on earlier levels of, and trends in, fertility rates; (2) Comparison of actual and expected births for the total population of an area including both participants and nonparticipants; and (3) Comparison of actual births among participants and a demographically similar control group. [15]

The first approach has the advantage of using data that is specific to the actual participants in the program and hence relatively free of extraneous "noise." Also, because the participants act as their own control group in the before and after comparisons there is little difficulty in ensuring demographic homogeneity between the groups being compared. The disadvantages of this approach are that it does not capture the catalytic effects that the program may have on outside groups, and that it requires more data than is often available. [16]

The second approach, which compares a larger population group before and after the program, has the advantages of capturing secondary or catalytic effects of the program and requiring little demographic data beyond that which is often readily available in government statistical reports. Such data may also give more complete indications of long-run trends in fertility than would data on program participants. The chief disadvantage of this approach is that factors that are unrelated to the program may have substantial influence on the ASFR for the larger group and give misleading indications of the effectiveness of the program. This is of particular concern when the program serves only a small part of the larger population group or when the larger group is in demographic disequilibrium. The latter situation is particularly evident in areas like Puerto Rico where large-scale internal and external migration is having a pronounced effect on the ASFR of many areas of the island.

The third approach, which uses a separate control group, has the advantage of allowing one to distinguish between effects that arise from the program and effects that are independent of the program. [17] The primary disadvantage of this approach is that it is time-consuming and expensive.

An important consideration in any of these approaches when the necessary data is not already available is the practicality of directly measuring the necessary ASFR.

Direct measurement of ASFR is often impossible or impractical because of the nature of, and amount of, demographic data required. First, there must be a large enough sample of women so that the before and after group fertility rates can be estimated with an acceptably narrow confidence interval.

Second, ASFR estimation requires that observations on patients span a period of months or even years. It is not enough to know the demographic state of a patient at a single point in time. One must instead know the patient's demographic state over a period of time including dates of important events such as live births. Because it is time-consuming to record such detailed demographic histories of patients, clinics often settle for a few demographic facts such as age, total number of live births (i.e., parity), date of last delivery, and sometimes, the ages of living children. In some situations rough fertility rates could be reconstructed from such demographic facts, but the process would be time-consuming and the results questionable.

Third, even if detailed demographic histories are available, it is difficult to convert this information into reasonable estimates of ASFR. For one thing, when women begin to participate in a family planning program they are almost all nonpregnant—an atypical state for a group of women. Where patients are largely referrals from post-partum clinics, it will be found that most have been pregnant during the last few months—another atypical situation. In order to estimate the fertility rates that would apply in the absence of the contraceptive program under study, it would be necessary to modify data derived from these demographic histories to take account of these atypical situations. Similar modifications would be needed to estimate ASFR after initiation of the contraceptive program.[18] In view of these circumstances, it is often impossible or impractical to estimate changes in fertility via direct measurement of fertility rates.

Direct Estimation of Births Averted: Potter's Approach

Robert G. Potter, Jr. reasons that a fertile woman may be in any one of three states at a given time: pregnant, amenorrheic, or fecundable.[19] His method focuses on the role of contraceptives in prolonging a woman's stay in the fecundable state. The actual method of calculating births prevented by the IUD is expressed in the equation:

$$B = I/D \qquad\qquad (3\text{-}18)$$

where

  B = births averted;

  D = average duration of marriage per birth in the absence of the contraceptive; and

  I = the length of average interruption of child-bearing— i.e., mean prolongation of stay in the fecundable state.[20]

Thus, if a married couple would have one child every 36 months in the absence of the IUD, and if its use keeps the woman in the fecundable state for an extra 12 months, then it is assumed that 12/36 or one-third of a birth will be averted over the 48-month period following insertion.

Potter makes adjustments for a number of demographic phenomena in calculating $\underline{I}$, including risks of infertility and secondary sterility, accidental pregnancy, interruption of marriage by death or divorce, or loss of the IUD as a result of explusion, removal, or pregnancy.

Potter's method is one of the most sophisticated approaches available, but it has some serious practical drawbacks. First, as Potter himself notes, it becomes an unwieldy computational task unless some simplifying assumptions are made.[21] Second, it requires many pieces of information which are often unavailable, such as the average interval between births, the risk of secondary sterility, and the risk of divorce.

These difficulties can be avoided with the less perfect but simpler "parity approach."

Direct Estimation of Births Averted:
The Parity Approach

The parity approach differs from the fertility rate approach in that ASFR are not measured directly but are estimated from parity data. It is a much simpler approach and probably gives equally accurate results under the data circumstances that apply in most family planning clinics, both in advanced and developing countries.

The parity approach uses the age and parity data commonly recorded on patient admission forms to construct a table or graph of average parity as a function of age of the clinic patients. Alternatively, the observations for all patients may be pooled and a continuous age-parity profile estimated by linear or nonlinear regression techniques.

With such a graph or table, the ASFR for women of age $\underline{A}$ may be found by computing the difference between the parities of women of ages $\underline{A}$ and $\underline{A} + 1$. The difference between these is the expected change in parity for women of age $\underline{A}$ during the next year or, equivalently, the expected ASFR for women of age $\underline{A}$:

$$\text{Parity}_{A+1} - \text{Parity}_A = E(\Delta\text{Parity})_A = E(\text{ASFR})_A. \quad (3\text{-}19)$$

If the age-parity relationship is represented as a continuous mathematical function, then the common, annual ASFR may be thought of as an approximation to the slope of this function between $\underline{A}$ and $\underline{A}$ + 1 on the age axis.

Given $E(ASFR)_A$, the number of births averted per acceptor per year may be calculated for age group $\underline{A}$ by multiplying this by the average monthly continuation rate (C_μ) and subtracting from this the product of the accidental pregnancy rate (P_a) for continuing users of that method (stated as the number of accidental pregnancies/woman-year of use), the number of woman-years of use $(C_\mu \times 1$ year or simply $C_\mu)$, and the ratio of live births to conceptions (B):

$$\text{Births averted} = E(ASFR)_A \cdot C_\mu - P_a \cdot C_\mu \cdot B. \qquad (3\text{-}20)$$
per acceptor per
year for group A.

It is here assumed that P_a is arrived at by direct observation rather than by "indirect estimation" from its theoretical components [e.g., by equations (3-15) or (3-16)].

There is an implicit assumption in the parity approach that patients visiting a particular family planning clinic are homogeneous in the sense that they all have the same demographic life cycle. There is an implication that in the absence of a contraceptive program the average 30-year-old woman of tomorrow would be demographically identical to the average 30-year-old woman of yesterday. How safe is this assumption?

It is well established that parity tends to vary not only with age but with motivation, income, race, and cultural characteristics. Patients who come to a particular clinic often live near that clinic, and as a result of voluntary and involuntary segregation in housing, are probably similar in income, race, and cultural conditions. In addition, the fact that patients bother to come to a clinic probably indicates that they have exceeded certain thresholds of need for con-traceptives and motivation to use them.

Where these factors do not impose sufficient homogeneity and where clinic records have detailed information on patients, the problem may be handled by subdividing patients into income, racial, or other groups and calculating age-parity profiles for these subgroups.

The most serious problem is not whether there are differences between people of the same age, but whether there are important generational differences. Do 20-year-old women today have the same desires for and abilities to produce or avert births that their mothers had at the same age? The answer is often no. In the United States, for example, the number of births per 1,000 women of age 20-24 and parity level 2 was 221 in 1940, 281 in 1960, and 175 in 1967.[22] Similar changes occurred in other age-parity categories. These changes are bound to lead to changes in the age-parity profile over time. If estimates of ASFR were to be made on the basis of age-parity profiles that were more than a few years old, or if ASFR were to be projected for a number of years into the future, such changes in the age-parity profile could lead to significant prediction errors.

However, such long-range predictions can often be avoided. Because the data needed for construction of an age-parity profile comes from clinic records rather than published statistics, the profile can be recalculated frequently and need not be more than a few months or, at most, a year old. With most contraceptive methods (except sterilization) planning decisions need not look more than one or two years into the future. This is true because low continuation rates and the practice of discounting tend to reduce the importance of benefits in the distant future relative to those in the near future, in the decision-making process. More important, with most methods, output decisions can be made for relatively short periods of time and reevaluated at the end of these periods. With methods such as the IUD, pills, condoms, etc. the clinic always has the option of discontinuing the service for a particular method/user combination if the costs are expected to outweigh the benefits in subsequent periods. Hence, the problem can often be reduced to one of estimating the expected change in parity between ages A and $A + 1$ during the next year on the basis of data that is six months or one year old. Since generational differences in the parity profile are not likely to be great between women who are only one year different in age, we should be reasonably confident of the results.

The major problem with the parity approach (or any other approach) is how to evaluate long-term methods such as sterilization. With sterilization, the program manager cannot decide each year whether or not to continue the service, but must instead decide once and for all at the beginning on the basis of the initial costs and the expected future stream of births averted. Because of uncertainty about the shape of the parity profile over long periods of time, there must be a substantial chance of error in estimating this future stream of births averted. If it is felt that the nature of change in the parity profile is adequately understood and if sufficient historical data is available, it may be possible to estimate the shape of the profile at various dates in the future and hence to make more accurate estimates of the change in parity. In the absence of such information, the program manager must simply base his decisions on the present profile, recognizing the danger of error in his estimate.

SUMMARY

This chapter has sought to elucidate a number of demographic variables such as fertility, failure, and continuation rates and to compare general methods of calculating births prevented which are based on these variables. While the methods offer a variety of degrees of complexity and accuracy, it has been argued that the parity approach is the most practical for evaluation of local programs, particularly in underdeveloped countries, because it requires data on only a few demographic variables such as age, parity, and the continuation rate— most of which are already collected on a routine basis.

4

PUERTO RICO,
POPULATION,
AND FAMILY
PLANNING

INTRODUCTION TO PUERTO RICO

Puerto Rico, the easternmost island of the Greater Antilles, is 1,000 miles southeast of Miami and 500 miles north of Caracas, Venezuela. The island is 105 miles long, 35 miles wide, and has an area of 3,435 square miles.[1]

The coastal portion of the island consists of a narrow, fertile plain while the interior is traversed by mountain ranges and deep valleys. Because of its subtropical to tropical climate the island supports sugarcane, pineapple, coffee, and tobacco.

Puerto Rico was discovered by Christopher Columbus in 1493 and subsequently settled by Ponce de León. The island remained a Spanish colony until the Spanish-American War in 1898 when it became a possession of the United States. American citizenship was granted to Puerto Ricans in 1917, and in 1952 a special commonwealth status was created for the island, giving it a greater measure of self-government while preserving its links with the United States.

The indigenous Arawak Indians died off quickly from diseases introduced by the Spanish settlers, declining in numbers from over 80,000 in 1508 to less than 4,000 in 1515.[2] Importation of black slaves was authorized in 1510 and, by the 18th century, there were enough on the island to support a modest sugar industry.[3] In 1802, these blacks accounted for 52 percent of the population.[4] With the abolition of slavery in 1873, color barriers gradually disappeared until now they are relatively unimportant except in the upper class.[5] Today the majority of Puerto Ricans are of Spanish descent, while about one-fifth have some Negro blood.[6]

Puerto Rico has made great strides in improving its economic and social conditions, as can be seen from Table 4.1. Gross production

TABLE 4.1

Net Income by Industrial Origin
(millions of current dollars)

	1950	1970
All industries	614	3,821
Agriculture	149	184
Manufacturing	89	953
Mining	1	11
Contract construction	27	321
Transportation and other public utilities	49	368
Trade	102	674
Finance, insurance, and real estate	52	442
Services	44	519
Government	70	618
Rest of the world	31	-269

Source: Puerto Rico, Oficina del Gobernador, Junta de Planificación, Informe Economico al Gobernador: 1970, p. A-4.

measured in current dollars has risen from $754.5 million in 1950 to $4,606.7 million in 1970.[7] Even in constant 1954 dollars the gain from $878.7 million to $2,814.0 million was impressive, and raised per capita gross product from $399 in 1950 to $1,051 in 1970 (1954 dollars).[8] During the period from 1960 to 1970 per capita personal income in Puerto Rico increased by 138.5 percent from $598 to $1,426 (current dollars)[9] while United States personal income per capita increased by only 75.8 percent.[10] At the end of this period, however, Puerto Rico's per capita personal income was only 36 percent of the U.S. average of $3,921 and only about 55 percent of that for Mississippi, the poorest state in the U.S.[11] Still, Puerto Rico's per capita GNP was higher than that of any Western Hemisphere country except Canada and the United States (see Table 4.2).

This increase in income has come about largely as a result of a tremendous expansion of manufacturing on the island. Gross annual fixed investment in plants, machinery, and equipment increased from $67 million in 1950 to $910 million in 1970.[12] Investment in human capital has also been great, as evidenced by the fact that annual expenditures on education and health by the Commonwealth government increased from $42 million in 1950 to $349 million in 1970.[13]

Puerto Rico's economic growth has brought with it great improvements in standards of living, particularly in terms of health, as

TABLE 4.2

Per Capita Gross National Product in Selected
Western Hemisphere Countries (in U.S. dollars)

	Per Capita GNP (1968)
United States	3,980
Puerto Rico	1,340
Venezuela	950
Mexico	530
Brazil	250
Jamaica	460
Haiti	70

Source: "1971 World Population Data Sheet," (Washington: Population Reference Bureau, Inc., 1971); based on 1968 data supplied by the International Bank for Reconstruction and Development.

evidenced by Table 4.3. Diseases such as diphtheria and malaria which are amenable to mass health programs have been almost wiped out. Many others have been greatly reduced.

In spite of these gains, Puerto Rico has serious economic and social problems, at least by United States standards. Unemployment ranged between 10 and 13 percent during the 1960s and was 10.8 percent in 1970.[14] It is reported that there are some 17,000 drug addicts on the island or about one for every 100 persons over 14 years of age.[15] The average number of students per teacher in public schools in 1966-67 was about 30 compared to 22 in the United States.[16] The rate of illiteracy in 1960 was equal to that of the United States in 1890—17 percent.[17] Finally, over 50 percent of Puerto Rican families earn less than $3,000 per year, or are living in poverty by U.S. standards.[18]

DEMOGRAPHIC CHARACTERISTICS OF
PUERTO RICO

The population of Puerto Rico has increased from about 80,000 in 1508 to 2.9 million in mid-1971.[19] During the first 400 years after the landing of Columbus, the population of Puerto Rico increased by less than 1 million. In the last 70 years, however, the population has increased over 1.7 million.

TABLE 4.3

Selected Death Rates for Puerto Rico

	1949	1968
Death rate[a]	12.2	6.3
Infant deaths[b]	78.5	28.6
Maternal deaths[b]	2.9	0.1
Tuberculosis[c]	179.4	15.3
Syphilis[c]	8.2	0.7
Dysentery[c]	3.6	—
Malaria[c]	11.8	—
Diphtheria[c]	4.0	—
Cancer[c]	56.8	87.7
Heart diseases[c]	106.5	146.2
Pneumonia[c]	119.9	34.3
Bronchitis[c]	12.3	1.9
Diarrhea-Enteritis[c]	183.2	11.8
Cirrhosis of liver[c]	11.7	19.9
Suicide[c]	21.5	8.6
Homicides[c]	14.6	7.0

[a]per 1,000 population
[b]per 1,000 live births
[c]per 100,000 population.

Source: Puerto Rico, Departamento de Salud, División de Registro Demográfico y Estadísticas Vitales, Informe Anual de Estadísticas Vitales: 1968.

The rate of growth of population in Puerto Rico during the 20th century has been a function of three different demographic variables— the birth rate, the death rate, and the emigration rate. As can be seen from Table 4.4, the death rate has fallen greatly since the turn of the century, with most of the drop coming during the 1930s and '40s. This was largely a result of public health programs. The birth rate has also fallen during this period, but the decline began later (in the 1950s) and has been more modest. This pattern is a typical example of the so-called "demographic transition" which has characterized advanced countries and which some social scientists expect to see repeated in less developed countries.[20]

In addition, the Puerto Rican situation is complicated by the presence of a third demographic force—large-scale emigration.

TABLE 4.4

Rates of Birth, Death, Natural Increase, Emigration, and Population Growth in Puerto Rico
(per 1,000 inhabitants)

Period	Birth Rate	Death Rate	Natural Increase	Emigration Rate	Population Growth Rate
1899-1910[a]	40.5[c]	25.3	15.2	—	15.2
1910-1920[a]	40.4[c]	24.0	16.4	0.8	15.6
1920-1930[a]	39.3[c]	22.1	17.2	2.6	14.6
1930-1940[a]	39.6[c]	19.6	20.0	0.5	19.5
1940-1950[a]	40.7[c]	14.5	26.2	8.8	17.4
1950-1960[a]	35.0[c]	8.0	27.0	19.9	7.1
1960-1965[a]	31.1	6.8	24.3	2.6	21.7
1966-1970[b]	28.1	6.6	21.5	9.0	12.5
1970[d]	24.9	6.5	18.4	-2.6	21.0

[a]Average annual rates. Data of Puerto Rico, Departamento de Salud, División de Registro Demográfico y Estadísticas Vitales as quoted in José L. Vázquez Calzada, "El Desbalance Entre Recursos y Población en Puerto Rico," (San Juan: Demographic Section, School of Medicine, University of Puerto Rico, November, 1966), p. 8. (Mimeographed).

[b]Average annual rates. Calculated from: Puerto Rico, Oficina del Gobernador, Junta de Planificación, Informe Economico al Gobernador: 1970, p. A-20.

[c]Not corrected for insufficient registrations.

[d]Annual rate. Calculated from: Informe Economico, p. A-20.

Emigration increased greatly during the 1940s and '50s, substantially reducing the population growth rate. In the early 1960s the emigration rate declined greatly and, as a consequence, the rate of population growth increased sharply. In the absence of emigration, Puerto Rico's population growth rate would have been between 2.4 and 2.7 percent in the 1950s and early 1960s (see Column 4 of Table 4.4) and in 1966 the population of Puerto Rico would have been over 3.3 million instead of slightly under 2.7 million.[21]

As a result of the great increase in population in Puerto Rico during the last 100 years, the island has become one of the most densely populated areas of the world (see Table 4.5). Puerto Rico now has almost 850 people per square mile or a population density 15 times as great as that of the United States. In the absence of emigration, Puerto Rico would now have over 1,020 people per square mile.

Because of Puerto Rico's high birth rate and low death rate, a large proportion of the island population is unproductive because it is either too young or too old to work. In 1970 it was estimated that 36.5 percent of the population was under 15 years of age and 6.5 percent over 64,[22] giving Puerto Rico a dependency ratio* of .76. By comparison, the dependency ratio of the United States was .62.[23]

THE BENEFITS OF BIRTH CONTROL IN PUERTO RICO

It is difficult to speak conclusively of the benefits of birth control in Puerto Rico, inasmuch as no complete study has been made of the relationships between Puerto Rico's demographic trends and its past economic development and future economic potential. However, it is possible to point to some of the relevant variables.

Production in any economy is dependent on the amount of natural resources, capital, and labor available and on the level of technology. Given the level of technology, per capita production is a function of the per capita amounts of resources, capital, and labor. If birth control can increase the per capita amounts of any of these resources, then it could result in higher per capita income—a clear benefit.

Puerto Rico, like any country, has a fixed amount of natural resources within its boundaries. The natural resources of Puerto Rico are not only fixed but rather modest. In the words of Dr. Vázquez Calzada:

---

*The ratio of the number of persons less than 15 or more than 64 years old to the number of persons 15-64 years old.

TABLE 4.5

Population Density of Selected Countries

Country	Population*	Area (square miles)	Population Density
Hong Kong	4,300,000	398	10,804
Netherlands	13,100,000	12,616	1,038
Taiwan	14,300,000	13,952	1,025
Puerto Rico	2,900,000	3,421	848
Japan	104,700,000	142,726	734
United Kingdom	56,300,000	93,898	600
Haiti	5,400,000	10,714	504
India	569,500,000	1,261,416	451
United States	207,100,000	3,615,211	57

*Estimated as of mid-1971

Sources: Areas are taken from Dan Golenpaul, ed., Information Please Almanac, Atlas and Yearbook, 1964 ed. (New York: Simon and Schuster, 1963). Population figures are estimates of the Population Reference Bureau, Inc. as reported in El Mercado de Valores, XXXII, 6 (February 7, 1972), pp. 125-128.

> Puerto Rico es un país de muy escasos recursos naturales. Un bonito paisaje, un clima relativamente agradable y un puñado de tierra exprimido y agotado por el monocultivo de la caña es prácticamente todo cuanto la naturaleza ha puesto a nuestro alcance.[24]

The population density of the island is now almost 850 people per square mile, a high figure in comparison with most of the rest of the world. However, high population density is not in itself a disaster as exemplified by New Jersey and Rhode Island which in 1970 had population densities of 953.1 and 905.4 respectively, but per capita incomes several times that of Puerto Rico.[25] New Jersey and Rhode Island are able to prosper in spite of their high population densities because they are rich in physical and human capital and are able to trade with other states, offering their services and manufactured goods in exchange for the food and primary products that they lack. By contrast, Mississippi, the poorest state in the union in terms of per capita income, had a very low population density in 1970—46.9 people per square mile.[26] Obviously, low population density is neither a necessary nor sufficient condition for prosperity.

Much of Puerto Rico's new private and public investment comes from outside the island—for example, 62 percent of its new investment in physical capital in 1965.[27] Direct private investment in Puerto Rico is probably a function of the profitableness of manufacturing in Puerto Rico—which, in turn, is a function of product prices on the U.S. mainland (the major market for Puerto Rican manufacturers), labor costs in Puerto Rico, and transportation costs between Puerto Rico and the U.S. mainland. Loans to the Commonwealth government are probably a function of the credit rating of that government which, in turn, is related to the government's ability to repay these loans as indicated by its present and anticipated tax revenues. Capital investment from local resources is probably a function of individual, business, and government saving rates and the profitableness of investments.

It is hard to see how any of the above sources of investment could be encouraged by a high rate of population growth in Puerto Rico. Much of the private investment in Puerto Rico is oriented toward export to the mainland and hence would not be influenced by the size of the Puerto Rican market. Individual saving is more likely to decrease than increase with a higher birth rate.[28] Finally, government revenues, and hence the government's ability to borrow outside of Puerto Rico, may be harmed by a higher birth rate if more dependents mean more tax exemptions for income earners.

Puerto Rican investment in human capital through expenditures on education and health is a function of government tax revenues and the ability of the government to borrow abroad. As indicated above, there is no reason to believe that a high birth rate would encourage either of these revenue sources.*

In short, if the population growth rate is high, per capita levels of human and physical capital at any point in the future are likely to be lower than if the population growth rate had been lower.

---

*One of the few existing quantitative studies of the benefits of family planning in Puerto Rico deals with the possible savings to the government from lower school enrollment in future years. While the "benefits" suggested by this study are impressive ($2,528-4,126 per birth prevented in present value terms), the study does not consider other important economic variables such as the present value of production lost when a person is not born, and hence presents only a partial answer to the cost-benefit question. See Kent Cline Earnhardt, "Population Growth and Educational Investment in Puerto Rico, 1970-1990" (unpublished Master's dissertation, Graduate Program in Planning, University of Puerto Rico, 1968).

The amount of labor services per capita is likely to be lower when population growth is rapid because a rapid rate of population growth increases the ratio of dependents to workers. This could be offset to some extent if larger family sizes induce family heads to give up leisure and offer more labor services. However, this effect is likely to be of little practical importance in Puerto Rico in view of current high rates of unemployment.

Finally, the level of technology in Puerto Rico is unlikely to be affected by population growth, inasmuch as most of the technology of the island is imported from outside the island.

In summary, it is difficult to see any way in which rapid population growth could have a significant positive effect on per capita quantities of natural resources, capital, or labor or on the level of technology. On the contrary, there is reason to suppose that rapid population growth would have a negative effect on these quantities, and hence on per capita income. Thus there is good reason to believe that birth control programs can have a beneficial effect in Puerto Rico, by raising per capita income.*

THE HISTORY OF FAMILY PLANNING IN
PUERTO RICO

Family planning has a relatively long but irregular history in Puerto Rico. The first family planning organization, the League for the Control of Natality, was founded in Ponce in 1925 by Dr. Lanauze Rolón but failed after only one year as a result of opposition from the Catholic Church and a lack of funds.[29] In 1932 another organization, the Birth Control League, was formed in San Juan by a lawyer and his wife, Estela A. de Torres.[30] Unlike the League formed in Ponce, this one did not limit itself to dissemination of information, but opened a clinic which offered contraceptives to the poor.[31] However, by 1934 it had also failed—and for the same reasons. In 1935, birth control information and contraceptives were made available in 53 clinics under the auspices of the Puerto Rico Emergency Relief Administration, an agency of the United States Government.[32] The popularity of the program, which was headed by Dr. José S. Belaval[33] — a

---

*Beyond these macroeconomic benefits, it is possible to point to other less dramatic benefits. It is estimated, for example, that a normal delivery and treatment of an abortion case in the government hospitals in San Juan cost $77.28 and $96.60, respectively. Interview with Dr. Antonio Hernandez Torres, July, 1969.

distinguished obstetrician—may be judged from the fact that 10,000
couples sought advice from the program during its first two years.[34]
In spite of its popularity, the program was discontinued in October of
1936, apparently as a result of political pressure during the months
before the 1936 presidential election on the mainland.[35]

In 1937, a group of social workers, physicians, and civic leaders
formed the Maternal Health Association and opened 22 clinics with
financial aid from Dr. Clarence Gamble.[36]

In the same year, the political and legal climate was greatly
improved by the enactment of Puerto Rico Laws No. 33 and 136. The
first of these amended the penal code canceling a clause that had made
the dissemination of contraceptives and family planning information
a felony. The second law authorized the Commissioner of Health to
offer maternal health services and family planning services through
the island health centers. The validity of Law 136 was upheld in
Federal Court in 1939, but the authority of the Commissioner to distribute contraceptives was restricted somewhat.[37]

In 1940, the Department of Health opened 122 family planning
clinics around the island. However, the 1940 elections brought a new
governor and a new Commissioner of Health to power and the program
gradually weakened.[38] In succeeding years the program waxed or
waned depending on the attitude of the governor and the Commissioner
of Health. At one point in 1947, the government was offering services
through 160 clinics.[39] At another point it virtually disavowed its
family planning programs, as in a statement of the governor's office
printed in El Mundo on March 8, 1949:

> It is not the policy of the Government of Puerto Rico to
> try to solve the problem created by the imbalance between
> the resources and the population of the country by con-
> traceptive means and much less by sterilization. Persons
> who express views to the contrary, although members of
> this government, speak strictly as private individuals.
> This government is trying to solve the discrepancy be-
> tween resources and the number of inhabitants by means
> of the 'battle of production.'[40]

Under continual pressure from the Catholic Church and other
groups, the Department of Health eventually adopted a laissez-faire
policy which permitted doctors and nurses to refuse to give contraceptive services if they objected to their use:

> Doctors, social workers and nurses are not required to
> recommend contraceptives or to help in the performance
> of sterilizations if for professional or any other reasons
> they disagree with the use of such methods.[41]

By 1954 the government program was at such a low ebb that a new private organization, the Asociación Puertorriqueña Pro Bienestar de la Familia (Family Planning Association of Puerto Rico), was formed to disseminate information and provide contraceptives. This organization was fated to repeat the up-and-down pattern set by family planning programs over the previous 30 years. The organization struggled along on a small budget for several years until large-scale support was obtained from the Sunnen Foundation in 1956. The Sunnen Foundation viewed the islandwide program as a demonstration project that would show the Puerto Rican Government what could be done. However, by 1963 the Government had shown little interest in taking over responsibility for the program and the Sunnen Foundation announced plans to withdraw its support. By 1965 the program had been drastically reduced and was serving only two areas of the island as opposed to 20 areas in earlier years.[42]

Since 1966, the Family Planning Association of Puerto Rico has been supported by substantial annual grants from the Office of Economic Opportunity.

In 1964 the Commonwealth Government began to play a more active role again when the Secretary of Health asked the Department of Obstetrics and Gynecology of the Medical School of the University of Puerto Rico to develop an effective family planning program for the Northeast Health Region. This request led to the combined post-partum, cytology, and family planning program that is the subject of this study.

5

DESCRIPTION OF THE PROGRAM

The postpartum, cytology, and family planning program operated by the Puerto Rican Department of Health in the Northeast Health Region consists of a central office located at the Centro Medico de Puerto Rico, in Rio Piedras,* and family planning clinics held at least once a week at 24 health centers, public health units, and subunits located in San Juan and other towns in the Northeast Health Region.[†] These clinics are staffed by three to four itinerant doctors and 14 graduate nurses who are employed by the program and who are sent from center to center to preside over the postpartum, cytology, and family planning clinics. When such a clinic is held, the host health center provides materials, physical facilities, and often the assistance of practical nurses and/or secretaries.

At centers where the number of patients needing services of the program is small, only one half-day clinic is held per week and all three services are offered at this clinic. Such weekly half-day clinics are the smallest production units that are feasible. It is not practical to hold clinics less than once a week because IUDs must be inserted

---

*A suburb of San Juan.

[†]While health centers, public health units, and subunits all have different health missions, these differences need not concern us; we shall refer to all of these health facilities as health centers. In this study, a family planning clinic is defined as the regular gathering together of various medical personnel and facilities for the purpose of dispensing contraceptives.

during menses. If clinics are held less frequently it becomes increas-
ingly difficult to see patients during menses. Furthermore, it is not
feasible to send the itinerant doctors and graduate nurses for less
than half a day because of the time and expense of traveling between
health centers.* There is thus an element of indivisibility in the allocation of doctors, graduate nurses, and physical facilities. This is
not true of the practical nurses and secretaries attached to the health
center who can be diverted from the family planning clinic to other
work at the health center when few patients appear or when the patients
who do come have been served.

At centers where the number of patients is large, two or more
half-day clinics may be held each week and these clinics may even be
specialized with some concentrating on postpartum examinations and
processing of new family planning patients and other clinics dispensing
oral contraceptives and serving cytology patients. An advantage of
such specialization is that factor inputs may be more closely tailored
to clinic needs. Follow-up and contraceptive services and cytology
services, for example, may be produced with only a graduate nurse
and a small physical plant. In addition, such specialization reduces
waiting time for these categories of patients, who can be processed
more rapidly than new patients.

Postpartum patients and those desiring a contraceptive are
handled in the following manner.[1] The program nurse arrives at the
center before the doctor and, with the assistance of one or more practical nurses or secretaries from the center, begins to interview each
patient about her medical, maternal, and contraceptive history. When
the doctor arrives, he gives all patients a group lecture on postpartum
care, contraception, breast and cervical cancer, and other hygiene
problems. In the course of the lecture he discusses the available
family planning methods, including the advantages and disadvantages
of each. At the end of this lecture a question and answer session is
held.

The doctor then sees the patients individually. He gives each
woman a physical and pelvic examination, takes a smear of cervical

---

*Strictly speaking, some of the parameters in this study could
be variables under other circumstances. Thus one might use probabilistic concepts and cost-benefit data to determine the optimal clinic
frequency. This is not feasible within the scope of this study inasmuch as the subject program is only one of many health programs
competing for health center facilities and, to a certain extent, must
harmonize with these other programs. Since these other clinics are
scheduled on weekly or multi-weekly bases, it would be inconvenient
to schedule the subject program on a 10-day basis, for example.

and vaginal tissue, and reviews the patient's history. A female employee of the program or the center is present during the examination
to assist the doctor and for legal reasons.

If the patient wants a contraceptive, she and the doctor reach
agreement on a particular method that is suitable in medical and
other respects. While a wide range of methods are made available,
96 percent of all patients selecting a contraceptive choose either the
IUD or oral contraceptives. If the IUD is selected and the patient is
menstruating, it is inserted at that time. If she is not menstruating
she is asked to return when she is. If she selects oral contraceptives
she need not be menstruating and is sent to the program nurse who
tells her how to use them and gives her a one-month supply. In addition to postpartum, cytology, and contraceptive services, patients
are frequently treated for minor vaginal infections or other complaints
and furnished with prescriptions ranging from vitamins to antibiotics.

Patients selecting the IUD are asked to return 6 weeks after
insertion, 6 months later, and then once a year. At each follow-up
visit the patient is examined to see if the IUD is still in position. Once
each year the patient is given a complete physical and a pap smear is
taken (cytology).

Patients selecting oral contraceptives return each month for
pills and have a full examination and pap smear at least once a year.

Where specialized clinics are held for follow-up oral contraceptive patients and patients desiring cytology, the clinic inputs generally consist only of the graduate nurse and a minimal amount of
facilities—often only a combination examining room and office. Patients are seen one at a time as they arrive.

Contraceptive patients fall into two main source categories:
postpartum patients who have delivered or been treated for an abortion
at the San Juan City Hospital or University Hospital and women from
the community. In the first category, women who accept family planning services within 3 months of the time that they leave the hospital
are referred to as "direct acceptors"; the others are referred to as
"indirect acceptors."[2] Direct acceptors are actively recruited through
lectures and interviews conducted at prenatal clinics and at the above
hospitals. There is no public information or recruitment program
aimed at indirect acceptors. These women must learn about the program by word of mouth.

Several types of records are kept for contraceptive patients.
A medical admission form is filled out for all patients. This form
is an important source of demographic information about patients
and includes items such as name, address, age, parity, years of
schooling, husband's occupation, and previous contraceptive experi-
ence. A full-page follow-up form is filled out each time an IUD patient
returns to the clinic. A separate follow-up form is not filled out for

each monthly visit by users of oral contraceptives because such visits usually involve no medical examination; instead, a reusable form is kept for each and monthly visits are recorded on consecutive lines of this form.

Beyond these patient records, a record called "Form A" is kept for each clinic showing the names of all patients seen during the week for postpartum examinations, initial visits for contraceptives, and follow-up IUD visits. In addition, Form A indicates the names of patients who changed methods, transferred from one health center to another or dropped out of the program, and the total number of pap smears performed each week.* This form is the key source of information on the number of patients of each type who were served each week at a given clinic.

ESTIMATION OF THE CONTRACEPTIVE
SERVICE PROCESS FUNCTIONS

In order to determine the cost of delivering contraceptive services, it is first necessary to determine the relationship between physical inputs and units of service produced. In the present situation it is not possible to estimate a production function—i.e., the relationship between outputs and all inputs. This is because the data available covers only a single multiclinic program under a single management. Since there are no empirical data on the amount of management per clinic and no other programs to compare, the role of the management input in production of contraceptive services cannot be determined by econometric techniques.

Given the impossibility of estimating a production function, the next best alternative is to estimate a "process function"—the relationship between outputs and all inputs exclusive of management.[3] With this, plus average figures on the amount of management per clinic or per patient visit, it should be possible to arrive at an estimate of the total cost per visit and eventually per birth averted.

The data available for study of the physical production relations consisted of (1) observations on inputs scheduled to be used by the postpartum, cytology, and family planning clinics in the subject program, and (2) weekly observations on the number of patients who received each type of service during the period from July 1 to December 31, 1968.

---

*This form does not contain the names of patients who received only pap smears.

Data on scheduled inputs for each clinic were obtained from interviews with the graduate nurse assigned to that clinic. They were asked what clinics were held each week during the above period, when the clinics were held, and what personnel were available. Four types of labor inputs were recognized: doctors, graduate nurses, practical nurses, and secretaries. Labor inputs were calculated on the assumption that morning clinics were 4 hours long and afternoon clinics 3 hours long and that scheduled personnel were available for the whole clinic.* Physical facilities were measured in "square-foot days"— i.e., the number of square feet available per day times the number of days. Floor space was measured at each clinic and it was assumed that both morning and afternoon clinics were of the same length—one half day. The last assumption is justified because of the difficulty of making any productive use of facilities during fractions of a half day. Hence, on an opportunity cost basis, there is no real difference between a 3-hour and a 4-hour clinic as far as facilities are concerned.

The major source of error in this data is likely to arise from the inability of the nurse to remember the level of inputs during the past (interviews were conducted 4 to 7 months after the end of the period under study). In most clinics, however, there had been few significant changes in inputs over the past year so that scheduled inputs at the time of the interview were the same as in the period under study.

Data on outputs were collected from the previously noted Form A. These were completed at the end of each week and are believed to be accurate records of services dispensed during that week. There were six major service categories: postpartum examinations, pap smears, new visits by either pill or IUD patients, and follow-up visits by pill or IUD patients. In addition, there were a number of special entries and minor types of service activities such as transfer of patient records to other clinics or classification of delinquent patients as "drops." These special entries were merged into one of the six previously mentioned service categories whenever input requirements were felt to be comparable. Where this was not possible, these were ignored as were certain minor service activities. This constitutes a source of error but was felt to be necessary to keep the problem manageable. It is not believed to be serious.

In collecting this output data it was evident that there was a serious danger of multicollinearity between either "postpartum

---

*Strictly speaking, the last assumption is not accurate since health center personnel can often be assigned to other tasks when there are no more contraceptive patients.

examinations" or "pap smears" and "new pill visits" or "new IUD visits" since all new patients are given both examinations and pap smears. In order to avoid this the first two categories were converted to a "net" basis by subtracting the total number of new visits from each of them. This meant that the "new visit" categories were now defined on a "gross" basis—including postpartum examinations and pap smears. The result was that the "net postpartum examinations" category was almost always zero or negative. It was therefore discarded as an output category. The remaining five categories—new and follow-up IUD and pill visits and net cytology (pap smears)—were retained. These are designated below as NI, FI, NP, FP, and NC, respectively.

A second data modification was necessary in order to allow for clinics that were closed as a result of holidays. Because clinic schedules indicated the day of the week when clinics were held, it was relatively easy to reduce clinic inputs to the proper level. No modification of clinic outputs was necessary. This adjustment of the data was not only necessary to increase the accuracy of observations but was also beneficial since it widened the scope of variation in inputs and outputs and hence supplied information on new areas of the process functions.

The first problem in estimation of a process function is to decide what functional form to use. This decision must be made on the basis of available evidence about key characteristics of the productive process such as the degree of substitutability between inputs and the extent of returns to scale.

In theory, it should be possible to substitute among the various inputs in production of contraceptive services—particularly among the labor inputs. In the present program, doctors, graduate nurses, practical nurses, and secretaries can all be used in the production of a given contraceptive service and their duties can be substituted for one another to a certain extent. However, substitution is actually confined to limited areas of the production process. In part this reflects limits in the productive abilities of factors. For example, all of the above personnel could fill out patient admission forms, but secretaries are not competent to take pap smears. Some of these limits could be removed through additional training, as in the case of graduate nurses who could be trained to perform many of the functions of doctors.[4] However, some limits to substitution appear to be due not to productive limitations but rather to understandings about who should carry out certain functions. Even if graduate nurses could be trained to competently carry out the principal functions of doctors, it is not clear that the medical personnel administering the program would be comfortable in allowing this because of the traditional emphasis of the medical profession on high quality standards. Finally the substitution is limited by the fact that some factors are complements rather than substitutes. In the present productive process the capital input—facilities—is rather simple, amounting to little more than building space and furniture such as desks, chairs, benches, and an examining table. Certain minimum amounts of space and equipment are needed to produce any given amount of output, but beyond these minimums extra space does not seem to have a great effect on productivity.*

The upshot of this is that, given the nature of the inputs and the administrative limits placed on them, it is probable that only a limited amount of substitution will actually be observed in the present program, irrespective of the possibilities that may exist theoretically. Substitution is most feasible in the less technical activities such as completion of forms, and hence most likely to be found among the lower grades of labor—graduate nurses, practical nurses, and secretaries.

The extent of scale effects will depend on the nature of the separate activities which compose the productive processes. Harvey Leibenstein distinguishes three different types of productive activities:

> (1) Direct proportional activities: those activities which are involved in operations on the commodity in question, and where the quantity of the particular activity is proportional to output. (2) Direct nonproportional activities: these are activities that are directly connected with producing the commodity but where the amount of the activity is not proportional to output. (3) Indirect activities: here we have in mind activities such as personnel administration, recordkeeping, and others that do not involve contact with the commodity but are necessary to the operation of the firm.[5]

Leibenstein argues that scale effects will not be observed unless the second and third types of activities are important in the productive process. In the present program, activities such as interviewing and examination of patients, final instruction in the use of methods, dispensing of pills, taking of pap smears, and maintenance of patient records are direct proportional activities and hence would not contribute to scale effects. Activities such as travel of personnel to and from clinics and group lectures to patients are direct nonproportional activities and could lead to scale effects. Finally, many aspects of program planning, administration, and evaluation; personnel

----

*It is likely, however, that the quantity and quality of facilities do have some effects on the willingness of personnel to work in, and patients to participate in, the program.

administration; purchase of supplies; and record maintenance would be classified as indirect activities.

All of the indirect activities listed above come under the general heading of program management and, as mentioned previously, cannot be included in the estimation process inasmuch as the data covers only one program. One of the two direct nonproportional activities— travel of personnel to and from clinics—is also not included in the data that will be used to estimate the process functions. Since this leaves only one activity that is not a direct proportional activity (i.e., group lectures to patients) and since this activity is involved in only two of the five outputs (new IUD and new pill visits), there is a strong presumption that the process functions will be characterized by constant returns to scale.

Before accepting this, however, it is well to reconsider the first list of activities and ask whether they are really direct proportional activities. Edward H. Chamberlin argues that an important cause of increasing returns to scale is increased specialization of factors.[6] Is this likely to be found in the present program?

The fact that there are four different types of labor used in family planning clinics is evidence of the belief by the program managers that specialization is possible. It is likely, however, that most of the gains from specialization will be realized in relatively small clinics. When a clinic is very small, it will be inefficient to provide it with a completely specialized team, given the fact that the itinerant doctor and nurse can visit only two clinics per day and hence will be unemployed when they have seen all of their patients. Since their opportunity costs will then be zero, it will be more efficient to have them do all of the work connected with the clinic rather than divert practical nurses or secretaries from other health center activities to help them. Therefore, because of indivisibilities in doctors and nurses we will expect very small clinics to be unable to take advantage of specialization possibilities and hence to have higher production costs.*

Once clinics have become large enough to justify a specialized team, there will be fewer possibilities for further specialization. This will be true for both technical and sociological reasons. From a

---

*The distinction between "large" and "small" is often a vague one. In the present context of indivisibilities and queuing, one might define a clinic as being "too small" if the vector of indivisible inputs for the optimum size clinic (as defined below) is less than the smallest nonzero vector of indivisible inputs that can be provided. In a larger sense, the existence of indivisibilities would seem to guarantee that clinics will almost always be "too small" or "too large."

technical standpoint the provision of contraceptive services is a relatively simple production process composed of less than a dozen separate activities each of which is not very complicated. It is therefore
doubtful whether further specialization would reduce costs significantly.

From a sociological standpoint it is possible that further specialization might have detrimental effects on the willingness of patients
to participate in the program. Reproduction and contraception are
rather intimate subjects for most people and program patients would
probably not enjoy being processed on an assembly-line basis.

Given these circumstances, it is probable that scale effects will
not be important in production of contraceptive services in the present
program and, to the extent that they are found at all, will probably be
associated with small clinics and with services to new patients.

In view of the nature of the present program, the most suitable
form for the process functions would appear to be one characterized
by constant returns to scale and limited factor substitution. A close
approximation to this is a mixed Leontief production function, similar
to those used by Martin S. Feldstein in his study of hospitals.[7] In the
present program this would have the form:

$$X_i = \min \,[B_1 D, B_2 F, B_3 f(GN, \ PN, \ S)] \qquad (5\text{-}1)$$

where X_i = number of contraceptive service visits of type i;

D   = hours of doctors' time;

F   = square-foot days of facilities;

GN = hours of graduate nurses;

PN = hours of practical nurses;

S   = hours of secretaries;

and where all inputs and outputs are measured on a per-week flow
basis. Such a process function would be characterized by constant
returns to scale and would not allow substitution between the three
main categories of doctors, facilities, and nurses-secretaries, but
would allow for substitution within the last category. The form that
the substitution will take within the latter class of inputs need not be
specified at this point. It is clear, however, that a Cobb-Douglas
form such as Feldstein uses is not entirely satisfactory inasmuch as
this implies that X_i must always be zero if GN, PN, or S becomes
zero—something that is not true of the present program.

The next problem is how to actually estimate the individual
process functions. This presents some difficulties because weekly
observations are stated in terms of total outputs and total inputs per

week for each clinic rather than individual outputs and associated inputs.

It was learned from the program director that at 22 of the 24 health centers, separate clinics using only graduate nurses and facilities are held for certain types of patient services.* In rural areas a separate clinic is held for follow-up pill patients and patients wanting only cytology services. In urban areas the separate clinics serve only follow-up pill patients.[8] If it is assumed that all urban follow-up pill patients and all rural follow-up pill patients and net cytology patients are served at these separate clinics where they exist rather than at the primary clinics, then the process functions for these two services can be separated from the process functions for the other three services. This can be, and was, done by estimating the process function for follow-up pill patients at the separate urban clinics, using this process function to reduce the inputs to the separate rural clinics by the amounts needed to provide the number of observed follow-up pill visits, and then regressing the rural net cytology data against the remaining inputs.

The urban data consisted of 26 weekly observations for each of eight clinics. After screening for dominance, the 24 most efficient observations were used to estimate the process function. The resulting function was

$$FP = \min [21.2GN; 0.555F]. \qquad (5-2)$$

The fit was very good as indicated by the fact that the adjusted coefficients of determination for the two regressions were 0.91 and 0.96, respectively.**

Next the process function for net cytology visits was estimated. The data for this consisted of 26 weekly observations for each of 10 rural clinics. After reducing the amounts of graduate nurse time and facilities inputs by the amounts that the above process function indicates were necessary to serve the actual number of follow-up pill

―――――――――――

*See pp. 51 for a previous discussion of this point.

**The reader is reminded that zero intercepts were imposed to conform with the assumption of constant returns to scale and hence correlation coefficients are computed about the origin rather than about the mean. Throughout this chapter, coefficients of determination are adjusted for degrees of freedom in accordance with A. P. Barten's procedure. See A. P. Barten, "Note on Unbiased Estimation of the Squared Multiple Correlation Coefficient," Statistica Neerlandica, XVI, 2 (1962) pp. 151-63.

patients seen by these clinics, the observations were screened for dominance. The 21 most efficient observations were then used to estimate the net cytology process function. This yielded the relationship

$$NC = \min[3.85GN; 0.0745F].$$

(5-3)

Once again the fits were very good with adjusted coefficients of determination of 0.94 and 0.80, respectively.

Estimation of the process functions for the other three types of visits (new IUD and pill visits and follow-up IUD visits) was more difficult. The most favorable data—that for the main rural clinics—consisted of observations on all three outputs and the total inputs available for all three outputs. It was thus impossible to estimate a separate process function for each of these outputs. The only alternative was to estimate a process function for the combined outputs.

The available information about the production of these outputs suggested that this was not necessarily a calamity. This is because the process functions for all three types of visits were expected to be of the same form:

$$X_i = \min[B_1D; B_2F; B_3f(GN, PN, S)].$$

(5-4)

In addition, there was reason to believe that all three would require roughly the same amounts of each input because several important activities were common to each production process.

The data consisted of 26 weekly observations for each of 13 rural clinics. After screening, this was reduced to 26 observations. Because of the paucity of undominated observations, it was not practical to experiment with elaborate hypotheses about the degree of substitutability within the nurse-secretary category. It was therefore decided that the most feasible function would be:

$$\Sigma (NI + NP + FI) = \min[B_1 D; B_2 F; B_3 GN + B_4 PN + B_5S].$$

(5-5)

The estimated function was:

$$\Sigma = \min[5.54 D; 0.125 F; 4.66 GN + 1.58 PN + 1.54S].$$

(5-6)

The adjusted coefficients of determination for the three parts were 0.92, 0.92, and 0.95, respectively.

Chow tests were then performed to assess the validity of the summation output form. Exploratory regressions were carried out with data subsamples which emphasized one or another of the three components of the summation output. It was observed that subsamples of observations in which the ratio NP: (NI + NP + FI) was high yielded higher regression coefficients than did subsamples of observations which emphasized NI or FI. It was therefore decided to split the original sample into two equal subsamples of 13 observations each, with one subsample composed of the 13 observations in which the ratio NP: (NI + NP + FI) was the highest and the other subsample containing the remaining 13 observations. Then the summation output was regressed against each of the three input groups using the two subsamples—first separately and then combined. Chow tests were then performed to determine whether there was any significant difference between the regression coefficients yielded by the two subsamples. The tests on the doctor and facilities coefficients indicated that it was not possible to reject the hypothesis that the coefficients were the same for the two subsamples, either at the 0.01 or 0.05 levels. In the case of the nurse-secretary coefficients, the hypothesis could not be rejected at the 0.01 level but could be rejected at the 0.05 level. Thus there is some statistical evidence to support the simple summation form which was chosen, but the evidence is not overwhelming.

ESTIMATION OF THE COST
OF CONTRACEPTIVE SERVICES

In order to calculate the per unit costs of contraceptive services one must know not only the relationships between physical outputs and inputs (i.e., the service process functions), but the unit cost of the inputs as well.

It was relatively easy to calculate the cost per hour of the four labor inputs. Average annual salaries for doctors and graduate nurses were calculated directly from salary data of the program, and those for practical nurses and secretaries were calculated from an annual salary report of the Commonwealth Government.[9] From this report and from interviews with administrators of the Puerto Rican Department of Health, it was decided that annual salaries should be increased by 11 percent to allow for fringe benefits. Finally, from information on paid vacations, holidays, paid sick time, and the length of the work week, it was estimated that the average government employee in the program was available for 1,449 hours in 1968. This figure was divided into the estimated figures on annual salaries and fringe benefits for each of the four categories to obtain the cost per hour of actual service. The results are shown in Table 5.1.

It was more difficult to calculate the value of a square-foot day of clinic space. Limited information was available on the construction cost of individual health centers in the Northeast Health Region.

TABLE 5.1

Estimated Cost Per Hour of Actual Work in 1968

Doctors	$8.84
Graduate nurses	3.31
Practical nurses	1.74
Secretaries	1.63

Using an index of construction costs, the total cost of each health center was converted to 1968 dollars.[10] Then a weighted index of the cost per square foot of construction was prepared from the estimated 1968-equivalent construction costs and information on the total floor space of each clinic. This yielded a construction cost of $27.59 per square foot in 1968 dollars. Assuming a 10 percent annual interest charge and straight-line depreciation over 20 years, yielded a depreciation and interest charge of $4.16 per square foot per year.

On the basis of information supplied by the Department of Health, it was estimated that the annual cost per square foot for electricity, water, and telephone services was $.47.[11] Combining this with the depreciation and interest figures yields a total annual cost of $4.63 per square foot. Finally, it was estimated that such facilities should have been available for a total of 247 working days in 1968. This yields a cost per square-foot day of $.01874.

Next, estimates were made of the costs of correcting certain side effects and the costs of the contraceptives themselves. The cost of a one-month supply of pills was $.59.[12] This must be added to the costs of both NP and FP visits. The cost of each IUD installation package was $1.75.[13] This cost is applicable only to NI visits. Finally, the cost of prescriptions needed to alleviate side effects attributed to the IUD is estimated at $.10 per FI visit.[14]

The final problem was to estimate the program management costs and to arrive at a scheme for allocating these costs. The labor overhead consisted of those personnel at the central office who were not engaged in research projects for outside agencies. Labor time devoted to such research projects was not included because the projects consisted primarily of data collection rather than data analysis and hence seemed unlikely to have immediate effects on productivity.

The total labor overhead cost, including fringe benefits, was estimated at $27,940. The annual cost of the facilities was estimated at $2,967 (641 square feet x 247 working days x $.01874). Finally, it was estimated that the equipment, desks, files, etc. for a program of this size would cost about $10,000.[15] Assuming straight-line depreciation of the equipment over a 10-year period and a 10 percent interest rate yields an annual interest and depreciation charge of $2,000. The total estimated overhead costs are thus $27,940 + $2,967 + $2,000, or $32,907.

An attempt was made to allocate the labor overhead costs by questioning central office personnel about their duties. On the basis of their replies it was decided that about 15 percent of the labor costs ($4,142) could be considered a function of program output and that the other labor and nonlabor costs were independent of the program output. The output-independent overhead costs must be considered in comparing the total costs and benefits of the program but they will not affect the choice of methods or users or the scale of the program since they do not affect the marginal costs of patient visits. Hence no attempt should be made to allocate these costs.

The output-dependent overhead costs, on the other hand, do affect the marginal costs of patient visits and should be allocated. It was evident that in the end some arbitrary allocation formula would have to be used. A decision was finally made to allocate these overhead costs over total annual patient visits. This formula is no less arbitrary than any other that might be tried but has the advantage that it does not create the impression that there are definite scale effects. If these overhead costs arise from direct nonproportional activities, then it is possible that there will be scale effects. However, the present data are not adequate to answer this question and hence it seems more reasonable to leave it to other researchers than to create a false impression. The results will therefore continue to show constant marginal costs, but the reader is reminded that slightly decreasing costs might be closer to the truth.

It was estimated that there were about 105,600 patient visits under the program in 1968 (84.6 patient visits per clinic per week on the average x 24 clinics x 52 weeks). Dividing this into the output-dependent overhead costs of $4,142 yields an overhead cost of about $.04 per patient visit.

Given the service process functions, the per unit costs of inputs, and the costs of contraceptives, prescriptions, and output-dependent overhead, it is now possible to estimate the minimum marginal costs of a unit of service. By minimum cost is meant the cost under ideal conditions, i.e., when inputs have been adjusted to output demands so that there is no excess capacity. This is done in Table 5.2.

Two comments are in order. First, it was found that although it is possible to substitute practical nurses or secretaries for graduate nurses in the production of the composite output, it is not economically advantageous to do so, given the present wage rates, and would not be desirable unless the wage rate for graduate nurses were at least 55 percent higher than at present.

TABLE 5.2

Minimum Marginal Costs of Contraceptive Service Visits

Type of Visit	Adjustments	Cost
New IUD	2,4	$4.25
New pill	1,4	3.09
Follow-up IUD	3,4	2.60
Follow-up pill	1,4	.82
Net cytology	4	1.15

Note: Assuming constant returns to scale and direct proportionality in the output-dependent overhead costs, the minimum marginal cost of a patient visit will not vary with the scale of output. The remaining overhead costs are assumed to be output-independent and amount to $28,765 for the year in question.

Adjustments:
1. Includes cost of pill pack = $.59
2. Includes cost of IUD pack = $1.75
3. Includes cost of prescriptions to alleviate side effects = $.10
4. Includes overhead cost of $.04

The continued use of practical nurses and secretaries in these activities is probably explained by the fact that the family planning program does not pay their salaries and hence has little incentive to husband them.*

Second, the reader is reminded that these costs have been estimated without regard to the queuing problem which is an inherent part of provision of family planning services. Given the high value of a birth prevented, a clinic operating under queuing conditions will want to have some excess capacity and hence will have specific marginal costs that are higher than the minimums indicated in Table 5.2.

---

*Of course, it is also possible that these personnel are underemployed at their health centers, and hence that their opportunity costs are less than their salary levels would suggest. In this case, it might be rational to divert them to the family planning program.

ESTIMATION OF
THE DEMOGRAPHIC VARIABLES

Because costs vary among different method-user combinations, it should now be clear that one cannot expect to arrive at universally true estimates of the cost of preventing a birth, but must recalculate the costs for each significantly different situation. In view of this, the present study does not seek to catalogue all situations and costs, but rather to provide a general method that will facilitate this calculation process.

The purpose of the following sections is to illustrate this method for a number of method-user combinations that were found at two clinics in the Northeast Health Region of Puerto Rico.

The first clinic selected was located in Bayamón, a relatively large urban area located about 15 miles southwest of San Juan. Bayamón had a population of 72,466 in 1960, an average family income of $2,347,[16] and a relative abundance of industry including sugar mills, an iron foundry, an oil refinery, and plants manufacturing automobile parts, machinery, and precision tools. The area surrounding the city is devoted to production of sugarcane, coffee, and a variety of fruits.

The second clinic was located in Toa Baja, a small town on the north coast of the island about 10 miles west of San Juan. In 1960 the town had a population of 19,700 and an average family income of $1,633 or only 70 percent of the Bayamón level.[17] In spite of the fact that 29 factories were in operation in Toa Baja in 1964, only slightly more than half of the town labor force was employed within the municipality.[18] While family incomes were lower than in Bayamón, most homes had electricity and running water.[19]

These two towns were selected for this study to illustrate the effect of differences in demographic characteristics on the cost of preventing births, including estimates of relevant demographic variables and data concerning the cost of preventing births at the two clinics.

Age/Parity Functions

The first relationship that needs to be considered is that between age and parity. It is known that parity tends to increase with age, but does it increase at a constant rate or at an increasing or decreasing rate?

If a group of women is observed from puberty through menopause, it will probably be found that parity for the group will rise at a constant or increasing rate at first as marriage and family formation proceeds, but will eventually rise only at a decreasing rate as the proportion of anovulatory cycles increases and sexual activity decreases. Thus, there is reason to believe that the age/parity relation will be nonlinear if the same group of women is observed through time.

It is unlikely, however, that an average woman in a family planning program will be the same as an average woman of the same age in the society as a whole or that the composition of a group of enrolling patients will remain constant over time. This is because patients have some ability to judge their need for contraception and to act accordingly. If a woman perceives a decline in her need for contraception because of widowhood, divorce, or early menopause, she may simply drop from the program. If this self-regulating process operates, the patients who are left in the program will tend to be those who are more fertile than the average.

Likewise, when a program is instituted, those patients who are in little danger of conception will not be attracted to it and the observed age/parity relation among those who do participate will be different from the age/parity relation that would exist for women as a whole.*

Therefore, the first empirical problem was to decide whether the parity function was linear or nonlinear. The data available consisted of observations on age and parity at the time of acceptance for 190 IUD acceptors and 191 pill acceptors at Toa Baja and 146 IUD acceptors and 204 pill acceptors at Bayamón. In order to test the linearity question, data samples for both clinics were split into separate groups according to age and linear regressions were run on both separate and pooled groups. Chow tests were then performed to see if the regression coefficients for young patients were significantly different from those for older patients. The results are shown in Table 5.3. The conclusion in all cases was that there was no significant difference at either the 0.05 or 0.01 level. Hence a linear form seems appropriate for the parity function.

Following this, a second hypothesis was considered: Is the parity function different for IUD patients than for pill patients?[20] This hypothesis was tested by regressions of parity on age for the separate IUD and pill patient samples and then for the two samples combined. Chow tests on these regressions revealed that there was no

---

*In making a decision about whether to participate, the woman will probably consider not only the changing probability of conception but the changing cost of conception as well. As noted earlier, one cost, the probability of maternal death, tends to increase with age and parity.

TABLE 5.3

Chow Tests of Age/Parity Functions

Comparison	Method	Clinic	Computed F*
Young v. old	Pills	Bayamón	.99
" "	Pills	Toa Baja	2.08
" "	IUD	Bayamón	2.50
" "	IUD	Toa Baja	.08
IUD v. pills		Bayamón	1.04
" "		Toa Baja	.74

$*F_{.05} = 3.00, F_{.01} = 4.61$

Note: When the computed F is lower than the critical level, it indicates that there is no significant difference between the regression coefficients for the two sets of data being considered, at that level of significance.

The test procedure is outlined in J. Johnston, Econometric Methods (New York: McGraw-Hill, 1963), pp. 136-38.

significant difference between the parity functions for the two methods at either clinic. The results are shown in Table 5.3.

The conclusion for the samples available is that the parity function is linear and does not vary with the method selected. The estimated results are shown in Table 5.4.

Contraceptive Continuation Rates

In Chapter 3, it was indicated that Mauldin and Zatuchni have both concluded that the continuation function relating the percentage of original IUD or oral contraceptive acceptors who are still active to time can be approximated by the general formula:

$$C = ae^{-rt}. \tag{5-7}$$

Preliminary regressions using data from a clinic at Ryder Memorial Hospital in Humacao, Puerto Rico, where oral contraceptives and IUDs have been offered since 1957 and 1961, respectively, supported this hypothesized form over what appeared to be the next best form—a reciprocal relation.

TABLE 5.4

Estimated Parity Functions for Toa Baja and Bayamón

		adj. R^2
Toa Baja:	P = -3.438 + .292A	.4469
	(.017)	
Bayamón:	P = -4.826 + .354A	.5120
	(.018)	

Note: The numbers in parentheses are the standard errors of the regression coefficients.

It was found, however, that the fit could be greatly improved if age were included as an explanatory variable. The most successful form found was:

$$C = ae^{-rM/A} \qquad (5-8)$$

where M indicates the number of months since acceptance and A is the age at acceptance. Table 5.5 shows the coefficients of determination for six sets of data using the decay form given in the literature (form #1) and the same form including age (form #2.)*

The age-modified form appears to be a great improvement over the simple decay form, as evidenced by the fact that the former has a higher coefficient of determination in five of the six cases, and raises the adjusted coefficients of determination by an average 26 percent.

More rigorous evidence of the superiority of the age-modified form was obtained by performing added-variable tests on the six sets of results. This test involves the comparison, via F ratios, of mean squares of the explained sum of squares added by inclusion of age in the regressions and the mean square of the residual sum of squares.[21] The results, which are shown in Table 5.6, indicate that the addition of age significantly improves the fit of the continuation function at the 0.01 level of significance in five of the six cases. In the case of the Humacao oral contraceptive group the results were not significantly

---

*In both forms, time was measured in months rather than years. Adjustments for patients who became lost-to-follow-up are given in the Appendix.

TABLE 5.5

Coefficients of Determination for Continuation Rate Forms
(adjusted for degrees of freedom)

Clinic Form	TB-I	TB-O	BN-I	BN-O	HU-I	HU-O
#1	.2429	.5021	.3676	.6507	.3370	.6710
2	.3844	.5851	.5749	.7189	.3977	.6487

Note: TB-I, BN-I, HU-I = Toa Baja, Bayamón, and Humacao
IUD groups, respectively.

TB-O, BN-O, HU-O = Toa Baja, Bayamón, and Humacao
oral contraceptive groups, respectively.

TABLE 5.6

Added-Variable Tests for the Age-Modified
Continuation Function

Clinic-Method Group	F ratio
TB-I	25.56
TB-O	21.21
BN-I	49.48
BN-O	33.09
HU-I	10.41
HU-O	6.73*

$F_{.01, 1, 100} = 6.90$
$F_{.01, 1, 150} = 6.81$

*Insignificant at the .01 level, but significant at the .05 level.

worse at the 0.01 level but were at the 0.05 level. The age-modified
form therefore appears to be an improvement over the simple decay
form.

The four Bayamón and Toa Baja equations that were estimated
using the age-modified decay function are shown in Table 5.7 in
common logarithm form.[22] The estimated regression coefficients
are highly significant in all cases and the results are appropriate

TABLE 5.7

Estimated Contraceptive Continuation Functions

Clinic-Method Group	Estimated Equation	Coefficient of Determination (adjusted for d.f.)	Sample Size
TB-I	log C = 1.946 - .222 M/A (.026)	.3844	116
TB-O	log C = 1.836 - .664 M/A (.054)	.5851	109
BN-I	log C = 2.045 - .256 M/A (.022)	.5749	104
BN-O	log C = 1.870 - .446 M/A (.024)	.7189	139

Note: The numbers in parentheses are the standard errors of the regression coefficients.

except for the Bayamón IUD equation (BN-I) which has an intercept that is slightly in excess of 100 percent.

Patient Visits Per Year

Interviews with the administrator of the program indicated that there were accepted norms about how often a patient should visit the clinic and that these norms depended on the method and the length of time the patient had been in the program. Users of oral contraceptives were expected to come once per year for a full medical examination which would be equivalent to a new patient visit and 12 times per year for follow-up visits to receive pills.* Because of data limitations there was no way to test the conformity of this service norm to reality. It was therefore assumed to be true. Thus pill patients were assumed to have the equivalent of one new visit and 12 follow-up visits per year.

---

*A total of 13 visits per year were needed because the average woman has 13 menstrual cycles per year and would hence need an equal number of packs of pills.

IUD patients were scheduled to have a full examination on the first visit and follow-up visits after 6 weeks, after 6 more months, and then once each year. Inspection of individual patient records showed that patients often deviated from this clinic regimen. Since data on visits by IUD patients were available, it was decided to regress the total number of visits for individuals against the number of months they had been in the program, assuming that the first visit was a new visit and that the others were follow-up visits. Adjustments for patients who became lost-to-follow-up were made in accordance with the procedure discussed in the Appendix.

Several facts were known about the probable shape of the total visit function. First, it should have a positive intercept value of one or more, and second, it should be monotonically rising. Besides this, there were two alternative hypotheses about the slope of the function. Total visits might increase at a steady rate over time, as suggested by the prescribed clinic regimen. This would suggest a linear relationship after the first year. Alternatively, it might be hypothesized that a portion of the acceptors would have difficulties with the IUD and initially require more frequent visits. Over time, these problems would either be resolved or the patient would become discontented and drop the method. Since both processes would lead to a group coming closer and closer to the prescribed clinic regimen, this would suggest a function that starts with a relatively steep slope and becomes flatter so that the function approaches linearity as $\underline{M}$ (months) rises. A form that meets this requirement of asymptotic linearity is:

$$V = a + B_1 M - B_2 \left(\frac{1}{M}\right) \qquad (5\text{-}9)$$

where $\underline{V}$ indicates visits and $\underline{M}$ indicates months elapsed since acceptance.*

An attempt was made to compare these two hypotheses by fitting linear and asymptotically-linear equations of the type shown above to 190 observations for Toa Baja and 223 for Bayamón. In both cases the asymptotically-linear regressions had slightly lower coefficients of determination and imperfections in the reciprocal term.** It was therefore decided that the more conservative hypothesis of linearity was a better description of reality in these cases. The linear results are shown in Table 5.8.

------

*The drawback with this form is that when $M = 0$, $V = -\infty$.

**One coefficient was insignificant. The other was positive in sign instead of negative.

TABLE 5.8

Estimated Visit Functions for IUD Patients

		adj. R^2
Toa Baja:	$V = 3.015 + .077M$ (.010)	.2522
Bayamón:	$V = 2.161 + .138M$ (.012)	.3735

Note: The numbers in parentheses are the standard errors of the regression coefficients.

Patient Arrival Probability Functions

What type of probability density function can best describe the arrival of patients at the family planning clinics?

Inspection of the literature indicated that production processes of the type evaluated in this study are commonly described by the Poisson probability function, which has the form:

$$P(X;\lambda) = \lambda^X \frac{e^{-\lambda}}{X!} \qquad (5\text{-}10)$$

where λ is the expected value of $\underline{X}$.

In order for the Poisson probability function to be considered appropriate in this particular problem there must be evidence that the probability of an arrival during a particular interval is (1) constant over time (i.e., statistically stable), (2) independent of previous events, and (3) independent of the length of the waiting line. These conditions are partially, but not completely, met in the program under study.

In order for the assumption of statistical stability to be considered valid it would have to be argued that the program was in an equilibrium with respect to the demand for its services. If the program were either expanding or contracting advertising and outreach programs and hence shifting its demand curve, or if autonomous forces outside the program (e.g., religious pressure, public opinion, changing moral standards, etc.) were shifting the demand curve, the assumption would be violated.

This possibility can be tested with some simple economic reasoning and an inspection of patient arrival data. One may first hypothesize that the demand for clinic services is a function of a variety of factors including patient tastes, travel costs, psychic costs, etc. as well as clinic charges. If all of these factors are held constant except patient charges, one expects the quantity demanded to be an inverse function of price as with most goods. This hypothesis is shown as D_s^1 in the figure below.

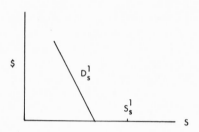

Inasmuch as the program under study had a fixed budget and was committed to supplying services at zero charges, its short-run supply schedule can be represented by a point on the abscissa.

Interviews with one of the program doctors indicated that it was very rare for a patient to be turned away without being served. This assertion, which is confirmed by the author's own observations and by data presented in Chapter 6, indicates that this supply schedule for a clinic usually lies to the right of the point where the demand schedule intersects the abscissa (e.g., S_s^1 in Figure 5.1).

If this is true, then the amount of services dispensed by any given clinic in the short run will be demand-determined. From this it follows that it should be possible to detect shifts in the demand schedule in the region of interest (the zero charge region) by simply observing the quantity of services dispensed per unit of time during the period in question. A simple test is to compare the average num-ber of units of service dispensed during non-holiday weeks at the beginning and end of the year for which data is available for the two clinics under study. Eighteen observations were selected for each method-clinic combination—nine from the period July through Septem-ber, 1968 and nine from the period from mid-March to mid-May of 1969. A simple nonparametric test, the Mann-Whitney test, was then made on each pair of samples.[23] These tests indicated that there was a significant difference between the average number of arrivals in the two periods in only one of the 10 method-clinic combinations (FI patients at Toa Baja) at the 0.05 level and in none of the cases at the 0.01 level. The assumption of statistical stability thus seems to be a reasonable one.

The second assumption was that the probability of an arrival during a particular interval is independent of previous events. It is clear than this assumption will not hold for a sample containing both new and follow-up patients using the same method since new patients beget follow-up patients. But if it is possible to separate new and follow-up patients, as in the present study, this need not be a problem.

A more relevant concern is the possibility of dependence of current follow-up visits on past follow-up visits. The program has a limited number of follow-up patients and hence a limited demand for follow-up services; if many of these patients seek follow-up services in any particular week it is possible that fewer will require these services in future weeks.

It is obvious that the question of independence turns on the nature of the demand for follow-up services. Part of this demand is likely to be of a stochastic nature as in the case of patients who are coming in response to side effects (e.g., the expulsion of an IUD) which have no relation to previous follow-up visits. In these cases, arrivals will be independent of previous events.

However, another part of the demand will tend to be associated with previous visits as in the case of oral contraceptive patients who must come to the clinic every month to obtain a supply of pills for the following month or IUD patients who have no complaints but come simply because the clinic personnel have recommended that they come once a year for a routine checkup. If the number of arrivals is large relative to the size of the pool of active patients, this dependence may be troublesome.

In the case of oral contraceptives, patients are required to come once every four weeks for supplies and therefore about 25 percent of the active patients must come in each week, on the average. In the case of IUD patients, the ratio of follow-up visits per week to active patients can be deduced from the visit functions that were estimated in the previous section. These revealed that the average IUD patient has 0.077 visits per month at Toa Baja and 0.138 visits per month at Bayamón. From this it can be shown that the ratio of FI visits per week to active IUD patients is 0.0178 at Toa Baja and 0.0318 at Bayamón or that about 1.8 to 3 percent of the active patients come in each week.

The upshot of this is that the assumption of independence does not hold for certain classes of follow-up patients, but the effect of previous arrivals on the probability of a current arrival depends on the method. The effect is likely to be much more serious in the case of oral contraceptives than in the case of the IUD.

The final assumption, that the probability of an arrival is independent of the length of the waiting line, is not completely satisfied in the present program in that patients are probably not indifferent to the expected waiting time or the probability of not being served. If this is so, then the probability distribution is not $g(X_a)$ but rather $g(X_a|X_c)$, i.e., the density function is affected by the capacity limit.*

One implication of this is that a direct statistical attack on arrival data is likely to yield $g(X_a|X_c*)$ rather than $g(X_a)$. How serious a difference is this?

As noted earlier, it was unusual for a patient to be turned away without being served. If this is true and if program patients realize this, then they should attach a value of nearly zero to the probability of being turned away, and hence the estimated $g(X_a|X_c*)$ should not differ greatly from $g(X_a)$.

It is not possible to test for the effect of X_c on $g(X_a)$ in the present program. This is not because of the lack of data on actual waiting times because proxies could easily be devised (e.g., the ratio of X_c to λ). It is rather because of the nature of the problem.

The density function, $g(X_a)$, is hypothesized to be a function of waiting time. Waiting time is in turn a function of the capacity of the clinic, X_c, and the demands on the clinic which may be represented by $g(X_a)$. According to the hypothesis we should expect a positive relationship between X_c and $g(X_a)$, since an increase in X_c will reduce waiting time and encourage more patient arrivals. But if the program directors are rational in planning the capacity of clinics, they will tend to provide more capacity at clinics with larger patient demands. Hence we may hypothesize that X_c will tend to be a positive function of $g(X_a)$.

Since causality runs in both directions between X_c and $g(X_a)$, a positive correlation between the two variables will not necessarily support either hypothesis. It will therefore be impossible to establish clearly the existence of an effect of X_c on $g(X_a)$ through cross-section data. What is needed are time series data for individual clinics that have changed X_c. Unfortunately, such data are not available for the present program.

Under these circumstances all that can be done is to estimate $g(X_a|X_c*)$ and proceed with the planning of efficient clinic capacity keeping in mind that $g(X_a)$ will have a tendency to move with X_c. If $g(X_a)$ is not very responsive to X_c then the substitution of $g(X_a|X_c*)$ for $g(X_a|X_c)$ may not be too serious.

In view of the above discussion, there is some doubt that the assumptions required for a Poisson function are fulfilled, particularly

---

*In order to avoid confusion $g(X_a|X_c)$ will indicate the general density function in which both X_a and X_c are variable, while $g(X_a|X_c*)$ will be used to indicate the particular form of the density function when X_c has the particular value X_c*.

in the case of FP patients, where the assumption of independence of previous events seems particularly dubious.

While it would be desirable to meet all of these assumptions, failure to do so is not necessarily a telling blow. As Milton Friedman has pointed out, a theory should not be tested by comparing its assumptions with reality, but rather by "seeing whether it yields predictions that are good enough for the purposes in hand."[24] In the present situation, the question is not whether there is exact conformity between the required assumptions and the present situation, but whether the divergence is serious enough to make the Poisson function unsuitable as an approximation to reality. The best way to answer this is to turn to the data and apply statistical tests to the hypothesis that a Poisson function is the correct function.

The data consisted of weekly observations on the number of patient visits produced at the Bayamón and Toa Baja clinics over the period from July 1, 1968 to June 1, 1969. Data at both clinics covered all of the five patient visit categories under study.

Since the theory of efficient allocation outlined in Chapter 2 can result in patients being turned away occasionally, there is some danger that the frequency distribution of patient visits produced will understate the frequency distribution of patient arrivals. However, as noted above, the surplus capacity margin in the program was such that patients were seldom turned away and hence the degree of understatement should not be very great. It is therefore assumed that the frequency distribution of patient visits produced is a close approximation to the frequency distribution of patient arrivals.

In order to test the hypothesis that the underlying probability functions were Poisson distributions, theoretical Poisson distributions were computed and compared with the observed frequency distributions.[25] The conclusion in nine of the ten tests of goodness-of-fit was that the null hypothesis could not be rejected at the 0.05 level.*

On the basis of this evidence it was concluded that the previously discussed disparities between the assumptions required for a Poisson function and the actual circumstances were not serious and that the Poisson distribution was an adequate approximation of the actual distributions.

---

*In view of the above discussion of independence from previous events, it is not surprising to find that the case that did not fit was for follow-up pill patients (at Toa Baja), the category in which the assumption of independence was considered most dubious. Further goodness-of-fit tests indicated that this frequency distribution could be approximated by a normal distribution; in this case the null hypothesis could not be rejected at the 0.01 level.

Since only the value of λ is needed to describe a Poisson distribution, the individual density functions may readily be found by substituting the estimated values of λ, shown in Table 5.9, into the standard formula for the Poisson function.

Accidental Pregnancy Rates

The final demographic variable that is needed is the accidental pregnancy rate, or the number of pregnancies per 100 woman-years of use.

Program data for the IUD showed 19 pregnancies for 8,949 woman-months of use during the first year and five pregnancies for 2,420 woman-months of use during the second year or accidental pregnancy rates of 2.55 and 2.48 for the two years.[26]

The data needed to calculate the rate for oral contraceptives were not available for the program. It was therefore decided to use the results of an earlier study of use of the pills in Puerto Rico which recorded 38 pregnancies in the course of 3,164 woman-years of use or a pregnancy rate of 1.2.[27] Because separate calculations were not possible for the first and second years, the calculated rate was used for both years.

CALCULATION OF THE COST
PER BIRTH PREVENTED

It is now possible to calculate the cost of preventing births. The first section below will deal with calculations for the two methods that are the primary focus of this study—oral contraceptives and the IUD. The second and third sections will deal with calculations for various methods of sterilization and Depo-Provera, respectively.

TABLE 5.9

Expected Number of Patient Visits Per Week (λ)

	Toa Baja	Bayamón
New IUD	1.00	5.38
New pills	3.53	17.00
Follow-up IUD	6.26	24.28
Follow-up pills	43.97	247.72
Net cytology	12.51	57.19

Oral Contraceptives and the IUD

Given the previously presented cost and demographic data, it is possible to calculate the minimum marginal cost of a birth prevented[28] for any combination of the following circumstances: (1) the IUD or pill, (2) patients at Toa Baja or Bayamón, (3) patients aged 15-44, and (4) patients in their first year or subsequent years. This amounts to several hundred possible combinations. However, the calculation process and important cost differentials may be illustrated by limiting the calculations to the 24 combinations possible from the two methods and clinics; ages 20, 30, and 40; and years one and two. Given the demographic functions used in this study, costs for subsequent years will be the same as those for year two.

The general approach will be to calculate the cost of supplying 100 initial acceptors with services for 1 year, to estimate the discounted number of births prevented as a result of the services provided during that year, and then to divide the former by the latter.

The number of births prevented by supplying services to 100 initial acceptors of age A for 1 year was calculated by combining formulas (3-19) and (3-20) of Chapter 3:

$$\text{Births averted per 100 acceptors per year} = \frac{100}{12} \left[(\text{Parity}_{A+1} - \text{Parity}_A) - P_a B \right] \left[\sum_{i=0}^{11} \frac{C_{Ai} + C_{Ai+1}}{2} \right] \quad (5\text{-}11)$$

where

P_a = the accidental pregnancy rate per woman-year of use;

B = the ratio of live births to pregnancies*; and

C_{Ai} = the continuation rate for age group A at the end of month i.

The formula has been adapted to allow calculation of births prevented on a monthly basis in order to minimize inaccuracies from the nonlinearity of the continuation function. This is the reason for division of the terms by 12 and for averaging continuation rates for the beginning and end of each month.[29]

---

*No data were available on B for Puerto Rico. It was therefore assumed to be 0.8, a figure that has been used for Taiwan. See W. Parker Mauldin, "Births Averted by Family Planning Programs," Studies in Family Planning, 33 (August 1968), p. 4.

The method of calculating service costs can best be illustrated with particular data. In the case of the IUD at Bayamón the total service costs for the first year for acceptors of age $\underline{A}$ were calculated by the formula:

$$TC = 100 \left[\$4.25 + \$2.60 \ (1.161a + 0.138 \sum_{i=1}^{12} C_{Ai}) \right] \quad (5\text{-}12)$$

where

$\$4.25$ = the cost per new IUD visit;

$\$2.60$ = the cost per follow-up IUD visit;

1.161 = the intercept of the IUD visit function minus one;

a = the intercept of the continuation function;

0.138 = the slope of the visit function; and

C_{Ai} = the continuation rate for age group $\underline{A}$ at the end of month i.

Total service costs for the second year are calculated with a modified version of this formula:

$$TC = 100 \left[\$2.60 \ (0.138 \sum_{i=13}^{24} C_{Ai}) \right] . \quad (5\text{-}13)$$

Total costs for other method-user combinations were calculated by substituting the appropriate data on continuation rates, visit functions, and costs per visit. In the case of oral contraceptives, the final term in the parentheses is summed over months 1 to 11 and is then multiplied by (12/11) to allow for the fact that the average woman has 13 menstrual cycles per year.

Finally, the costs per birth prevented were calculated by dividing the total cost per year per 100 acceptors by the total number of discounted births prevented as a result of these services. Births were discounted to allow for the fact that there is a 9 month lag between conception and birth and hence expenditures today do not result in prevented births until 9 months from now. The final problem, that of picking a discount rate, was solved by performing the calculations for discount rates of both 5 and 10 percent. The results, after rounding to the nearest dollar, are shown in Table 5.10. Discussion of the results will be found in Chapter 6.

TABLE 5.10

Minimum Marginal Cost Per Birth Prevented:
IUDs and Oral Contraceptives

Clinic	Age	Year	Births Disc. at 5%		Births Disc. at 10%	
			IUD	Pills	IUD	Pills
Bayamón	20	1	$37	$46	$39	$47
		2+	13	41	14	43
	30	1	35	45	36	46
		2+	13	40	14	42
	40	1	35	44	36	45
		2+	13	39	14	41
Toa Baja	20	1	54	61	56	63
		2+	9	53	10	55
	30	1	52	58	54	60
		2+	9	51	10	53
	40	1	51	57	53	59
		2+	9	50	10	52

Note: Costs are the same for all years after year 1; hence the designation of such years by "2+."

Male and Female Sterilization

Calculations were next made of the cost of preventing birth by sterilization. Two methods were evaluated: (1) female sterilization via tubal ligation, and (2) male sterilization via vasectomy.

The data for the first case consisted of cost accounting information for public hospitals at Centro Medico de Puerto Rico, in San Juan.[30] The estimated costs of tubal ligation were:

Doctor - 1.5 hours	$ 5.73
Room and board - 2 days	49.50
Operating room	88.30
Anesthesia	19.46
Recovery room	17.35
	$180.34

The only item that is likely to excite interest, the doctor cost, is based on costs for third-year resident physicians who earned $731.25 per month and reportedly worked at least 60 hours per week. The resulting hourly figure was raised by 11 percent to allow for fringe benefits.*

The cost of a vasectomy was estimated at approximately $150 based on replies from a questionnaire sent to private urologists in the city of San Juan. Because of the small number of positive replies and the fact that those contacted were specialists, the results are uncertain and probably represent a higher cost and higher quality treatment than the average person would obtain.

Estimates of the number of births prevented were made using the parity data for Toa Baja and Bayamón. In order to provide a reasonable cutoff point for the stream of births prevented, it was assumed that parity increased up until the age of 45 at which time menopause occurred. In the case of vasectomies the age used is that of the wife rather than the husband. As in the previous section, births were discounted at rates of both 5 and 10 percent.

The minimum average cost per birth prevented was calculated by dividing the cost of the sterilization by the discounted total of births prevented. The results, rounded to the nearest dollar, are shown in Table 5.11. The figures shown are minimum average cost figures as opposed to the minimum marginal cost figures given in Tables 5.10 and 5.12. This is because the cost data for the sterilization methods include overhead management costs while the data for the nonsterilization methods do not. Like the figures for nonsterilization methods, these figures are "minimum" cost levels in the sense that the queuing problem is assumed away, rather than in the usual economic sense of the minimum point of a traditional long-run average cost curve.

Depo-Provera

The last method to be evaluated, Depo-Provera, is an injectable contraceptive developed by the Upjohn Company which is being tested in Puerto Rico. The contraceptive inhibits ovulation in the same way that oral contraceptives do and can give contraceptive protection for periods from three months to a year, depending on the dosage level. Detailed continuation rate and cost data was not available for this method, but because of the promise that it shows as a future method

---

*The marginal cost of a tubal ligation at the time of a cesarean section was found to be very low. There was no evidence of extra expenses for room and board, the operating room, or anesthesia. The extra cost of the recovery room ($5.78) and an extra half hour of doctor time ($1.91) brought the total to only $7.69.

TABLE 5.11

Minimum Average Cost Per Birth Prevented:
Female and Male Sterilization

Clinic	Age	Births Disc. at 5%		Births Disc. at 10%	
		Tubal Ligation	Vasectomy	Tubal Ligation	Vasectomy
Bayamón	20	$36	$30	$56	$47
	30	49	41	67	56
	40	118	98	135	112
Toa Baja	20	44	36	68	57
	30	60	50	81	68
	40	143	119	162	135

of contraception, it was felt that rough calculations of the cost of preventing births by this method should be included in this study.

Accordingly, estimates have been made for both 3 month and
6 month injections of Depo-Provera. Because of the speculative
nature of the estimates, an attempt was made to bracket the true
costs with optimistic and pessimistic estimates rather than to pin-
point them.

The cost of an initial visit was taken to be about the same as
the basic cost of a new IUD or pill visit ($2.50), plus the cost of the
injection, which was estimated at about $1.15 for the 3 month form
and $1.73 for the 6 month form.[31] The basic cost of a follow-up visit
was assumed to be $.50, (about twice as much as for a follow-up pill
visit) plus the cost of the injection. Finally, it was assumed that
patients would have the equivalent of one initial visit per year and
either three or one follow-up visits per year depending on which form
they received.

The number of births prevented was estimated for patients having
the parity functions of Toa Baja and Bayamón. The continuation rate
problem was solved by performing the calculations for two situations:
(1) an optimistic situation in which all acceptors continued until the
end of the year, and (2) a pessimistic situation in which all acceptors
dropped out after the first injection wore off (i.e., after 3 or 6 months).
The accidental pregnancy rate was taken to be 0.24 per 100 woman-
years of use (a figure supplied by Upjohn),[32] and $\underline{B}$ was again assumed
to be 0.8.

As before, the cost per birth prevented was calculated by dividing
the estimated cost of supplying services to 100 acceptors by the estimated number of discounted births prevented as a result of these

TABLE 5.12

Minimum Marginal Cost
Per Birth Prevented: Depo-Provera

		Births Disc. at 5%		Births Disc. at 10%	
Method	Clinic	Opti-mistic	Pessi-mistic	Opti-mistic	Pessi-mistic
3 month	Bayamón	$25	$43	$26	$44
	Toa Baja	31	52	32	54
6 month	Bayamón	19	25	19	26
	Toa Baja	23	30	24	31

services. The results, rounded to the nearest dollar, are shown in Table 5.12.

The results of this and the two previous sections are discussed in the following chapter.

PLANNING CLINIC CAPACITY

In Chapter 2 it was argued that if the clinic manager wishes to maximize net social benefits, he will raise clinic capacity (X_c) to the level where

$$MC = E(MB) = V_p B_a \sum_{a=c+1}^{\infty} g(X_a). \qquad (5\text{-}14)$$

The purpose of the present section is to demonstrate how one may solve for the optimum level of X_c, given V_p, B_a, MC, and $g(X_a)$. In order to illustrate the approach, optimum capacity levels for follow-up pill patients will be calculated for Toa Baja.

The minimum marginal cost of an FP visit has already been estimated to be about \$.82 and $g(X_a)$ [really $g(X_a|X_c)$] is known to be a Poisson distribution with a mean of approximately 44 for Toa Baja (see Table 5.9).

The value of a birth prevented (V_p) in Puerto Rico is unknown. However, if one accepts Stephen Enke's rough calculations that a birth prevented is worth about 2.6 times per capita output, then the value of a birth prevented in Puerto Rico in 1968, based on the population and current GNP data presented in Chapter 4, should have been about \$3,600.[33]

The last piece of information, B_a or the expected number of births averted per follow-up visit, presents a problem inasmuch as both new and follow-up visits are needed in order to prevent births and there is no unambiguous way of allocating the actual births prevented between the two methods. It was finally decided to allocate the births on the basis of the ratio of FP costs to total costs (FP + NP) during the first two years. On this basis, approximately two-thirds of the births prevented were attributed to FP visits and the other one-third to NP visits. Multiplying this by the ratio of total births prevented to total FP visits (a constant in this case) yielded a B_a of 0.0178 for Toa Baja.

Substituting these values into equation (5-14) yields

$$\$.82 = \$3,600 \cdot 0.0178 \cdot \sum_{a=c+1}^{\infty} g(X_a) \qquad (5\text{-}15)$$

$$\sum_{a=c+1}^{\infty} g(X_a) = 0.0128 \cdot \qquad (5\text{-}16)$$

Assuming again that the parameters of the probability function of patient arrivals do not change as X_c is changed, one may simply consult a table of the cumulative Poisson probability function and find the value of $\overline{X}$ at which the cumulative probability that the number of arrivals exceeds $\overline{X}$ is 0.0128 when λ is 44. The result is an optimum clinic capacity of about 60 FP visits. If the estimated FP process function is given by equation (5-2), the clinic manager will have to provide $60/21.2 = 2.8$ graduate nurse hours and $60/0.555 = 108$ square-foot days of facilities in order to make sure that he will have sufficient capacity 98.7 percent of the time.

NET BENEFITS OF THE PROGRAM

Based on the assumptions and estimates made above,* the total benefits of the program in terms of births prevented can be calculated by forming the product of the total number of births prevented and the value of a birth prevented.† Since the latter has been taken to be

---

*The reader is urged to regard this estimate as no more than tentative, inasmuch as no detailed calculation of the value of a birth prevented has been attempted in this study.

†No attempt will be made to estimate the value of cytology services.

$3,600, the only problem is that of estimating how many births have been prevented.

Because there were no estimates of the demographic variables for all the patients in the program, it was decided to use the demographic estimates that had been prepared for Bayamón and Toa Baja and, on the basis of these, to prepare two alternative estimates of the number of births prevented.

The number of births prevented among oral contraceptive users can be estimated by multiplying the slope of the parity function by the total number of woman-years of use and subtracting the number of births resulting from accidental pregnancies. Woman-years of use can be calculated by summing the total number of pill packs dispensed during the year and dividing by 13 (because women have 13 menstrual cycles per year on the average). Births resulting from accidental pregnancies can be found by multiplying the accidental pregnancy rate by the number of woman-years of use and B divided by 100.

The total number of woman-years of use was estimated to be 6,547 (i.e., 85,106 pill packs dispensed ÷ 13). Using the parity function slopes for Toa Baja and Bayamón (0.292 and 0.354, respectively), the accidental pregnancy rate of 1.2 per 100 woman-years of use, and $\underline{B}$ = 0.8, it was estimated that the number of births prevented among oral contraceptive users was 1,833 by the Toa Baja estimate and 2,239 by the Bayamón estimate.

Births prevented by the IUD were arrived at in an analogous manner, except that woman-years of use were calculated by dividing the total number of follow-up IUD visits during the year by 12 times the slope of the IUD visit function. This yielded 7,249 woman-years of use for the Toa Baja estimates and 4,045 for the Bayamón estimates. Applying the respective parity slopes, the accidental pregnancy rate of 2.5 per 100 woman-years of use and $\underline{B}$ = 0.8 yields 1,936 births prevented by the Toa Baja estimates and 1,331 births prevented by the Bayamón estimates.

Thus the total number of births prevented is calculated to be 3,769 by the Toa Baja estimates and 3,570 by the Bayamón estimates. Assuming the value of a birth prevented to be $3,600, the total benefits are $13.57 million and $12.85 million by the two estimates.

The total costs of the program for one year were estimated to be about $231,000 distributed as follows:

Doctors	$ 46,887.36
Graduate nurses	67,298.92
Practical nurses	8,776.56
Secretaries	6,357.00
Facilities	15,536.04
Overhead	32,907.00

Contraceptives	52,953.04
Prescription costs	669.80
Total	$231,385.72

Subtracting the total costs from the two estimates of total benefits leaves net benefits at $13.34 million by the Toa Baja estimate and $12.62 million by the Bayamón estimate.

6

**RESULTS
AND
RECOMMENDATIONS**

The purpose of this chapter is to unite the diverse theoretical and empirical elements of the study and to present the policy implications of these results. In particular, it will seek to: (1) summarize the economic and demographic findings of the study, (2) make recommendations for improvements in the Puerto Rican program and others like it, and (3) make recommendations for further research on the costs of preventing birth.

SUMMARY OF RESULTS

Production and Cost Relationships

In the study, arguments were presented to support the contention that the production process for contraceptive services can be described by a mixed Leontief process function of the form

$$X_i = \min [B_1 D, B_2 F, B_3 f (GN, PN, S)] . \qquad (6\text{-}1)$$

Such a form is believed to be appropriate for the program under study, because the production processes appear to be characterized by: (1) constant returns to scale, (2) limited substitutability among the major input categories (doctors, nurses, and facilities), and (3) relatively free substitutability within the nurse-secretary category. Support for these assertions took the form of theoretical reasoning and observation rather than actual empirical tests.

Two important conclusions were reached with respect to service production. First, there was empirical evidence to suggest that the

program under study should use graduate nurses rather than practical
nurses or secretaries, given the apparent productivities and present
wage rates of these types of labor. Second, it was found that follow-up
visits are less expensive than initial visits for both IUD and oral
contraceptive patients.

Demographic Relationships

Regressions of parity on age and Chow tests indicated for both
Toa Baja and Bayamón that the parity function was linear and that its
slope did not differ between groups that had selected different methods.

Nonlinear regressions of the continuation rate on time for clinics
at Toa Baja, Bayamón, and Humacao indicated that the decay form
presented in the literature provided a better fit than did the next best
alternative—a reciprocal form. It was found, however, that the fit of
the continuation function could be improved when age was included as
an explanatory variable. The most suitable form was found to be:

$$C = ae^{-rM/A} \quad . \tag{6-2}$$

Regressions of total IUD visits on time since acceptance (in
months) indicated slightly better results for a linear form over the
other theoretically justifiable form, an asymptotically linear equation
of the type:

$$V = a + B_1 M - B_2 \left(\frac{1}{M}\right) \quad . \tag{6-3}$$

Finally, tests indicated that the patient arrival probability function could be approximated by a Poisson distribution:

$$P(X; \lambda) = \frac{\lambda^X e^{-\lambda}}{X!} \quad . \tag{6-4}$$

This hypothesis was supported in nine out of ten goodness-of-fit tests
for Toa Baja and Bayamón.

Cost Per Birth Prevented

The most fundamental conclusion of this study is that costs
vary substantially among different method-user combinations. Holding
other things equal, costs varied by a factor of 1.5 between clinics, by

a factor of 3 between ages, and by a factor of 6 between methods. Overall, costs varied among different method-user-clinic combinations by a factor of up to 18.

Before attempting to compare costs between different methods, several comments must be made. All of the cost figures are minimum cost figures, i.e., they all abstract away from the problem of queuing. Thus the figures for oral contraceptives and the IUD assume that output needs are known exactly and hence inputs need not be in excess. Each figure for these two methods is, in effect, the value of marginal cost at the minimum point on the monotonically-increasing marginal cost curve which could be derived from equation (5-14) if V_p and B_a were held constant and X_c were varied. Although it has not been discussed explicitly, the queuing phenomenon should also be found in the other methods and hence the figures for these methods represent minima in a similar sense.*

The cost figures differ in that the two methods of sterilization include overhead management costs and hence are average cost figures while the figures for the other methods do not include these costs—and are hence marginal cost figures. Thus costs are not strictly comparable between the sterilization and nonsterilization methods.

Finally, the cost figures for Depo-Provera are hypothetical figures and must be read with skepticism.

Even with these caveats in mind, several conclusions about the costs of specific methods in use in Puerto Rico seem justified. The IUD prevents births at lower cost in all cases considered in this study than does the oral contraceptive because of its lower maintenance costs and its higher continuation rate. The two methods of sterilization—tubal ligations and vasectomies—are competitive with the IUD or the pills when administered to relatively young patients but are not competitive if the woman is more than 30 to 35 years old.** The competitiveness of sterilization methods for patients in their late 20s or

---

*Note that the marginal cost curves that can be derived from equation (5-14) are monotonically-increasing because of queuing, not because of the law of variable proportions or because of scale effects in the production process. All productive processes in this study have been treated as characterized by constant returns to scale.

**Certain potential costs such as psychological side effects of sterilization are omitted from the calculations, but should be considered when sufficient data become available. In the meantime, decision makers must make a subjective evaluation of these costs.

early 30s depends on the rate at which births are discounted: the lower the discount rate used, the lower the relative cost of sterilization methods. Thus if births are discounted at 5 percent, vasectomy is a cheaper method than oral contraceptives for 30-year-old women at Toa Baja, but if a 10 percent rate is used this conclusion is reversed. When the choice is between vasectomies and tubal ligations, the former is always cheaper because of its lower initial cost. The important factors with sterilization methods are the length of the prospective stream of births prevented and the high initial cost of the method. Finally, rough calculations suggested that the 3 month version of Depo-Provera would be more economical than oral contraceptives, that the 6 month version would be competitive with the IUD, and that if a 12 month version were developed it might be more economical than any of the methods examined. More data on the extent of follow-up visits for side effects might alter these results, however.

With respect to users, it would appear that it is slightly cheaper to prevent births among older women than among young women when the IUD or pills are used because older women have higher continuation rates. However, it is more expensive to prevent births among older women when sterilization is used because they have shorter streams of potential births.

With respect to time, it was found to be cheaper to prevent births with the IUD or pills after rather than before the patient's first year. In the case of oral contraceptives, this was because of lower drop rate after the first year, while with the IUD it was due to the lower average frequency of visits after the first year.

A comparison of costs between the two clinics revealed that it was cheaper to prevent births at Bayamón than at Toa Baja with all method-user combinations except the IUD (after the first year). The generally lower costs at Bayamón are explained by the facts that: (1) the slope of the parity function was steeper at Bayamón than at Toa Baja (0.354 v. 0.292) and hence more births were prevented per unit of service, ceteris paribus; and (2) the continuation rate for oral contraceptive patients was higher at Bayamón than at Toa Baja. Toa Baja had lower costs with the IUD after the first year, primarily because it had a lower frequency of follow-up IUD visits than did Bayamón.

The present writer does not feel competent to try to explain these demographic differences and will leave this task to sociologists and demographers. The differences are probably due to differences in the inherent characteristics of the populations of Toa Baja and Bayamón and/or differences in the quality of service at the two clinics. With respect to the latter factor, the higher rate of follow-up IUD visits at Bayamón may be due to the fact that this clinic was open more hours per week and hence more convenient for patients.

Finally, it is interesting to compare the cost of preventing a
birth by contraception and by abortion. In 1969, the cost of an abortion
at the public hospitals in San Juan was estimated at $96.60.[1] If, as
assumed in this study, only eight live births result from every 10
conceptions, this means that it costs $120.75 to prevent a birth by
abortion. It would thus seem that abortion is not only a controversial
method of birth control but an expensive one as well.

RECOMMENDED PROGRAM IMPROVEMENTS

How can the economic efficiency of the Puerto Rican family
planning program and similar programs be improved? Some
suggested changes are already in effect in Puerto Rico, and have been
included here for the benefit of persons concerned with other programs.

The first and most obvious implication of this study is that clinic
managers should seek to set their inputs and hence output capacities
at the optimum levels in order to maximize net social benefits. In
the case of the Puerto Rican program there are indications that
capacity is set too high. In Chapter 5 it was calculated that the
optimum weekly input levels for follow-up pill service at Toa Baja
should be 2.8 hours of graduate nurse time and 108 square-foot days
of facilities. Even allowing for the input needs of net cytology service
and for indivisibilities, it is clear that the actual input levels of 7
hours of graduate nurse time and 468 square-foot days of facilities
are excessive.* Similar calculations for follow-up pill service at
Bayamón show optimum input needs of 16.7 graduate nurse hours and
640 square-foot days of facilities while actual endowments were 52
graduate nurse hours, 1,904 square-foot days of facilities, 26 practical
nurse hours, and 26 secretary hours. Again this seems excessive
even allowing for net cytology demands and indivisibilities.

A caveat is in order, however. In the calculations of optimum
clinic capacity it was assumed that the value of a birth prevented was
$3,600. If the true value is much higher than this, then the observed
capacity levels may be more reasonable. Only a complete study of
the value of a birth prevented in Puerto Rico can answer this question.

A second series of recommendations deals with the queuing
phenomenon. The problem of predicting output levels is an in-
escapable feature of any organization that must dispense service to
the public. No matter what is done, there will always be an element
of uncertainty in planning output levels. However, a number of steps

---

*The endowments are those for periods during the week when
the doctor was not scheduled to be at the clinic.

can be taken to reduce the degree of uncertainty or to reduce the economic waste that results from fluctuations in service demands.

The first approach is to try to reduce the variance of patient arrivals. The simplest way of doing this is to disseminate information on clinic office hours so that prospective patients will know exactly when clinics are scheduled to open and close. Another way is to offer appointments for follow-up patients and, where possible, for new patients.* This has the effect of making output more predictable for at least a short period into the future. It also has the advantage of reducing waiting time and thus perhaps increasing the average number of patient arrivals or increasing the continuation rate.[2]

A second general approach to the queuing problem is to try to reduce the economic waste from fluctuating demand. It has been assumed in this study that the number of clinics and their locations are given. However, in certain cases it may be possible to reduce the waste from excess capacity by combining two or more clinics. A simple example will illustrate this. Assume that $MC \div V_pB_a = 0.111$ and that there are two identical clinics, each having an expected number of patient arrivals of four per week. The benefit maximizing capacity levels for each of these clinics will then be 7.0. But if the two clinics could be amalgamated into one with an expected number of patient arrivals of eight per week, the efficient capacity level would be only 12.0 or two less than when the two clinics were separate. In this particular case the same level of benefits could be achieved with a lower sacrifice of resources if the clinics were combined. This result, which rests on the law of large numbers rather than on any assumption of increasing returns in the process function, offers one possible way of reducing the waste associated with queuing. Before such mergers are attempted, however, other potential costs such as the toll in resources and patient demand from increased travel time should be considered.

There are two other ways to reduce the waste associated with queuing. A common way of doing this is to have program personnel work on their patient records or other paper work during slack periods. A more novel approach is to request that clinic personnel stay until all patients who come are served and, in turn, allow them to go home early when few patients come. Such an arrangement may be most advantageous for the clinic even if employees must be paid extra to compensate for the annoyance of a fluctuating workday.

The third series of recommendations deals with indivisibilities and the scale of operation. As indicated in the beginning of Chapter 5,

---

*This approach is used in clinics operated by Planned Parenthood of Houston.

facilities and personnel cannot be easily used in less than half-day units. As a result, some small clinics are chronically overstaffed. One solution to this problem is to hold clinics less frequently so that average attendance will be higher. As indicated in Chapter 5, however, it is difficult to hold clinics less than once a week because of the need to insert IUDs during menses, and it is difficult to have clinics on intermediate time bases—e.g., every 10 days—because of the need to harmonize with other users of facilities.

Fortunately, there are other ways of alleviating this problem. Once simple approach is to attempt to attract more patients by advertising.[3] While birth control is a sensitive topic, there are subtle and low-key methods available.

Another approach which is now being tried in Puerto Rico is to merge the family planning program with related programs. The original program took account of this principle by combining post-partum, cytology, and family planning activities. More recently this program has been merged with another program charged with offering maternal and infant care services. While it is possible that combining additional services into single clinics will reduce efficiencies fostered by specialization and division of labor, it is likely that the benefits from increased utilization of inputs at small clinics will outweigh any detrimental effects.* At large clinics, the advantages of specialization and division of labor can, of course, still be pursued.

In Chapter 5 it was found that it was not economically advantageous to use practical nurses and secretaries in place of graduate nurses in production of the composite output (NP + NI + FI) given the relative wage costs and productivities of these labor categories and would not be advantageous unless the wage rate for graduate nurses were at least 55 percent higher than at present. Because those results are based on a process function that aggregates together three kinds of outputs, one cannot be sure that the present practice of using practical nurses and secretaries is wasteful, particularly if they are under-employed in their other health center activities. However, the results should be investigated, and if confirmed, the use of these labor categories under present circumstances should be reconsidered.

In addition, it is recommended that the program management investigate the possibilities of training low wage categories of labor to take over the work of more expensive personnel. One solution to

---

*Another important advantage of such a merger is that it should emphasize the role of contraception as a legitimate part of the pro-creation-child raising process and thus make it more acceptable to patients, clinic personnel, and the general public.

the nurse-secretary problem raised above would be to provide additional training to practical nurses and secretaries so that their productivity would be high enough to justify their use in the program.

Another possibility would be to train graduate nurses to take over the work of doctors in providing contraceptive services. It would probably be relatively easy to teach them the mechanics of pelvic examinations and insertion of IUDs, but activities such as diagnosis of gynecological or other conditions that affect the choice of contraceptives would require more training. The author is not competent to judge in this area and can only recommend that the possibilities be examined.

Finally, it is recommended that the Commonwealth of Puerto Rico consider expanding the program under study to take in the other four health regions of the island. No detailed estimates of the resources needed to do this are made here inasmuch as this has already been done elsewhere.[4] Suffice it to say that the net benefits of such an expansion are likely to be very great.

Before such an expansion is carried out, however, a study should be made of the private program operated by the Family Planning Association of Puerto Rico, which presently serves these areas (cf. Chapter 4). Since this private program dispenses services in a fundamentally different manner, the relative efficiency of its operations should be evaluated before any move is made to displace it with a traditional clinic system. It might, for example, be more efficient for the government simply to encourage this program to expand its services by granting it subsidies.

RECOMMENDATIONS FOR FURTHER RESEARCH

The purpose of the present section is to point out areas in which additional research is needed and to warn future investigators of pitfalls that the present writer has discovered.

The most general need is for more evidence on the productive and demographic relationships that have been investigated so that it will be possible to decide whether the results of the present study represent essential truths or only the situation in one special area of the world. Are parity functions for program participants generally linear? Is the IUD visit function usually linear? Does age usually enter into the continuation rate in the manner found in this study? What is the effect of X_c on $g(X_a)$?

Of most interest for economists will be the question of the form of the process functions. It has been argued in this study that the process functions should be mixed Leontief forms. It has not, however, been possible to really prove this assertion empirically due to data deficiencies. More studies of the degree of factor substitutability and of returns to scale are needed before this question can be answered conclusively.

In this regard it should be noted that there are two forms of "economies of scale" that should be examined. The first are technical economies of scale that might occur in the input-output relationship. It has been argued that the process functions involved in the study should exhibit constant returns to scale. However, this has not been proven empirically and is a fitting area for further research.

The second type of "economies of scale" arises from the law of large numbers. As was demonstrated in this chapter, it may be possible to combine two clinics and provide an optimal capacity level with fewer total resources than are required when clinics are separate. More study is needed of the potential gains from such mergers.

Several recommendations are in order for future studies of the productive relationships. First, there is a need for estimates of the production function as opposed to process functions. This is not likely to be an easy task even if data on more than one program are available because of the presence of queuing and joint production. Second, estimations of process functions can probably be done better by using industrial engineering techniques to collect input-output observations rather than by screening weekly observations. The former approach will probably make it possible to avoid much of the dominance problem and will permit a much closer and more confident approximation of the true process function. This approach will also make available more detailed data on specific input-output combinations, and will thus make it easier to discover the degree of factor substitutability. Once an undominated data sample is available, regression techniques may be applied as in this study.

There is also a need for studies of other approaches to dissemination of contraceptives. Jamaica, for example, has made extensive use of commercial facilities to disseminate traditional contraceptives. The Family Planning Association of Puerto Rico disseminates clinical methods of contraception, but contracts with local private physicians to provide services in their own offices on an appointment basis.

Finally, there is need for research on other aspects of allocation of family planning funds in Puerto Rico. In Chapter 5 it was estimated that the net benefits of the program in 1968 were on the order of $12-13 million. However, the most important figure in these calculations, the value of a birth prevented, was a very crude estimate based on an extrapolation of Enke's theoretical results. At present, the only study of the benefits of population control for Puerto Rico is that of Kent Cline Earnhardt (see Chapter 4). In that study, Earnhardt projected alternative birth rates for Puerto Rico from 1970 to 1990 and estimated the savings in educational expenditures that would follow from reductions in the birth rate. While the study seems to be well conceived and executed, it is only a partial answer to the problem of estimating the value of a birth prevented in Puerto Rico. There are other benefits besides savings in educational expenditures—e.g., savings in expenditures for public health, law enforcement, utilities, etc. Against these positive benefits one must weigh negative benefits such as the value of the production lost when a person is not born. There is obviously room for much more research in this area.

Beyond the static problem of calculating the costs and benefits of preventing births now, there is a dynamic allocation problem that must be considered.* What is the optimum birth rate for Puerto Rico? Will the value of a birth prevented change substantially as the number of births prevented per year rises (and hence the population growth rate falls)? If so, the practice of discounting births prevented as outlined in Chapter 1 and the procedures for planning efficient clinic capacity would have to be modified substantially. As corollary questions one might ask what will happen to the costs of raising children (e.g., scale effects in public education) or wages in the future if the program is highly successful.[5] Even the discount rate used to convert future births into equivalent numbers of present births may be affected by the rate of growth of population. Since this rate is really society's rate of social time preference (i.e., its observed trade-off between present and future consumption) it is possible that a change in the rate of population growth will change society's view of the merits of the future, relative to the present. If, for example, population growth accelerates and is expected to bring a deterioration in the quality of future life through overcrowding, famine, pollution, and the threat of greater violence, then society may tend to lower its subjective valuation of the future relative to the present or, equivalently, may tend to discount the future at a higher rate. In terms of the present study, society would then exhibit an increasing preference for the resources freed by present births prevented over an equivalent amount of resources released by future births prevented and hence would have a relatively greater preference for births prevented now.

If this is true, then it will be appropriate to reconsider the old discount rate from time to time to see if it is still in keeping with the society's current assessment of the future. The present author does not expect to see answers to these questions in the near future given

---

*The author is indebted to Professor Donald Huddle for suggesting many of the points in this paragraph.

the theoretical and empirical weaknesses of present techniques for estimating the value of a birth prevented or the effect of demographic changes on wages and the discount rate. But unless we are so pessimistic as to feel that we can have little effect on the aggregates that determine the value of a birth prevented, we should begin to think about these questions.

In conclusion, it should be noted that there is ample evidence in the literature that birth control by almost any method is a high-return investment. In spite of this the funds available are limited and must be used as wisely as possible. It is hoped that this study and the ones that have been suggested can play a role in doing this.

GLOSSARY OF SYMBOLS

A - age (in parity and continuation functions)

A_v - the percentage of women in an age group who are "available," i.e., not pregnant or lactating

a - a constant indicating the percentage of patients who continue in a contraceptive program beyond their first visit

ASFR - age-specific fertility rate

B_a - the expected number of births averted per unit of service dispensed (patients served)

B - ratio of live births to conceptions

BN-I - IUD patients at Bayamón

BN-O - oral contraceptive patients at Bayamón

C - the continuation rate, i.e., percentage of initial contraceptive acceptors who are still active at a given time

D - the number of days that a woman is infertile as a result of pregnancy or lactation

D - hours of doctor time

e - the natural logarithm base

F - square-foot days of facilities

ΣF - the total failure rate (generally use-related failure)

ΔF_i - change in the age-specific fertility rate for age group i as a result of use of contraceptives

FI - follow-up IUD visits or patients

FP - follow-up pill (oral contraceptive) visits or patients

$g(x_a)$- the probability density function of patient arrivals

$g(x_a|x_c)$ - $g(x_a)$ when the clinic capacity is set at x_c patient visits

GN - hours of graduate nurse time

HU-I - IUD patients at Humacao

HU-O - oral contraceptive patients at Humacao

I_f - installation-related failure rate, i.e., the ratio of faulty contraceptive installations to total installations

IUD - intrauterine device

M - the number of months since acceptance of a contraceptive

MB - marginal benefits

MC - marginal cost

NC - net cytology visits or patients

NI - new IUD visits or patients

NP - new pill (oral contraceptive) visits or patients

P - the parity, or number of live births, by a woman

P_a - accidental pregnancy rate (stated as the number of accidental pregnancies per 100 woman-years of use)

PN - hours of practical nurse time

r - the continuous rate of decline in the continuation rate

R^2 - coefficient of determination

S - hours of secretary time

t - in continuation functions, time expressed in years

TB - total benefits

TB-I - IUD patients at Toa Baja

TB-O - oral contraceptive patients at Toa Baja

TC - total cost

V - in visit functions, total IUD visits

V_p - the present value, in dollars, of a birth prevented

W - the number of women in an age group

X_i - number of contraceptive service visits of type i

X_c - the output capacity of a clinic

X_s - the number of units of service dispensed or, equivalently, the number of patients served

Y_i - number of units of input i

Z_p - fecundability, or the probability that a susceptible nonpregnant woman will conceive on a given day

λ - expected number of patient arrivals

Δ - change in

Note: Symbols used between pp. 34-5 have not been included because they are not used outside of that section.

GLOSSARY OF TERMS

Accidental pregnancy rate (Pa). The number of accidental pregnancies per 100 woman-years of use of a contraceptive.

Age-specific fertility rate (ASFR). The number of births to women of a certain age group during one year, divided by the number of women in that age group.

Contraceptive continuation (or retention) rate (C). The percentage of initial contraceptive acceptors who are still active at a given time.

Contraceptive method. Any means or practice which serves to decrease fecundability.

Effectiveness of a contraceptive method. The relative reduction in fecundability produced by use of a contraceptive.

Family Planning Clinic. The regular gathering together of medical personnel and facilities for the purpose of dispensing contraceptives.

Fecundability (Z_p). The probability that a susceptible nonpregnant woman will conceive on a given day.

Parity (P). The number of live births to a woman; birth of live twins would raise parity by two.

Process function. The technically efficient relationship between outputs and inputs, with the exception of management.

LOST-TO-FOLLOW-UP ADJUSTMENTS

At any given time after acceptance, IUD patients may be classified as active, dropped, or lost-to-follow-up (LFU). Active patients are ones attending a clinic at regular intervals and either have their IUD in situ or are seeking to have it reinserted. Dropped patients are ones who have appeared and asked to have the IUD removed or, if it has been expelled, have declared that they do not want it reinserted. Patients classified as LFU are those who have simply stopped coming to the clinic. It is therefore not known for these patients whether the IUD is still in place, has been expelled, or has been removed by another physician. Inasmuch as 31 percent of the Toa Baja IUD patient sample and 34 percent of the Bayamón IUD patient sample were classified as LFU at the time of the study, it was decided that some data modification should be made to allow for these patients.

The only information on LFU patients as a group was a study conducted by program personnel in June, 1968. In this study, a total of 76 patients previously classified as LFU were located and interviewed. Of these, 46 were found to still have the IUD in place (hereafter referred to as LFU actives) while 30 had expelled it or had it removed (LFU drops). A preliminary inspection of the data suggested that the percentage of those in the latter category tended to increase with the amount of time elapsed since the patient stopped attending clinics. An attempt was therefore made to regress the percentage of LFU drops against time since disappearance from the program.

Three data procedures were used. First, patients were grouped into four-month intervals (working back from the date of the interview) according to the date when they became LFU. Then the percent of LFU drops was computed for each group and paired with the time in months from the class mark to the interview date. Second, the data were arranged in equal size groups working back from the interview date. In this case, time was measured from the class mean rather than the class mark. Finally, a moving average of the data as defined in the last procedure was used.

In all three cases, simple linear regressions with origin forces were used and in all three cases the regression predicted that 100 percent of the LFU patients would become LFU drops at the end of about 44 months.

On the basis of this evidence, it has been assumed throughout this study that patients who become LFU retain the IUD for 22 months (the assumed average) and then have it removed by a physician outside the program. This solution is an obvious weak link in the study inasmuch as (1) it is based on a small sample of LFU patients, (2) the LFU sample available was not drawn scientifically to reflect special age or other characteristics, and (3) only a minority of the LFU patients sought were ever found and interviewed. However, there was no other choice, given the data deficiencies. It is not felt that any inaccuracies in the LFU adjustment used here will change substantially the calculations in which it plays a role—calculation of visits per year and continuation rates.

THE COSTS OF SIDE EFFECTS

Contraceptive side effects have featured prominently in the literature and cannot be ignored in a study of the costs of preventing births.

These side effects range from minor ailments such as nausea, headaches, and weight gain associated with oral contraceptives to more serious problems such as pelvic inflammatory disease associated with the IUD,[1] and very serious problems such as thromboembolic disease associated with oral contraceptives.[2] Some, such as psychological side effects arising from sterilization can probably never be put into dollar terms,[3] while others, such as thromboembolic disease, can some day be valued but not until better information on incidence is available.

The total costs associated with the most serious side effects are probably less than those associated with the more minor side effects because of the low incidence of the former. Pelvic inflammatory disease, for example, affects about 2.5 percent of IUD patients during the first year and about 1.5 percent during the second year,[4] but the excess mortality rate from thromboembolic disease is estimated at only about three deaths per 100,000 women per year.[5] Because of this low incidence and the difficulties of accurately measuring incidence and assigning costs, major side effects are not evaluated in this study. The remainder of this discussion is therefore limited to minor side effects.

Many of the costs of minor side effects are labor costs incurred when a patient comes to the clinic to complain, and have already been captured through the estimates of cost per visit and the frequency of visits. An associated cost which has not been considered is the cost of prescriptions for treatment of these conditions. Such prescriptions are primarily associated with the IUD rather than with oral contraceptives.

In order to estimate the cost of prescriptions required for treatment of IUD side effects, a total of 537 follow-up visit sheets were examined for IUD patients at Bayamón. On the basis of consultation with a program physician, it was decided that of the 286 prescription notations found, 27 were for conditions caused by the IUD, 177 were for conditions probably not caused by the IUD, and 82 were for conditions which might have been caused by the IUD. For lack of better information, it was arbitrarily assumed that half of the last category of prescriptions were needed for correction of IUD-caused side effects.

The total cost of IUD-caused prescriptions was then computed. Where exact costs were not available, it was assumed that each prescription cost $1.50. On the basis of these assumptions, the total prescription cost associated with these 537 visits was calculated to be $53.77 or slightly more than $.10 per follow-up visit.

CHAPTER 1

1. Minoru Muramatsu, "Japan: Miracle in East Asia," in Bernard Berelson, ed., Family-Planning Programs: An International Survey (New York: Basic Books, 1969), p. 17; Gerald Zatuchni, "International Postpartum Family Planning Program: Report on the First Year," Studies in Family Planning, 22 (August 1967), pp. 17-18; Benjamin Viel, "The Social Consequences of Population Growth," PRB Selection No. 30 (Washington: The Population Reference Bureau, 1969), p. 2.

2. When More is Less (New York: Planned Parenthood Federation of America, 1968), pp. 10-14.

3. This theme is pursued in Ansley J. Coale and Edgar M. Hoover, Population Growth and Economic Development in Low-Income Countries (Princeton, N.J.: Princeton University Press, 1958); empirical evidence that aggregate savings rates are a function of dependency ratios and hence birth rates are presented in Nathaniel H. Leff, "Dependency Rates and Savings Rates," The American Economic Review, LIX, 5 (December, 1969), pp. 886-96.

4. Hla Myint, "The 'Classical Theory' of International Trade and the Underdeveloped Countries," in James D. Theberge, ed., Economics of Trade and Development (New York: John Wiley and Sons, Inc., 1968), pp. 203-4.

5. W. Parker Mauldin, "Births Averted by Family Planning Programs," Studies in Family Planning, 33 (August 1968) p. 1.

6. As quoted in S. N. Agarwala, "Evaluating the Effectiveness of a Family Planning Program," in Clyde V. Kisner, ed., Research in Family Planning (Princeton, N.J.: Princeton University Press, 1962), p. 410.

7. David R. Seidman, "Costs and Effectiveness of Alternative Modes of Delivering Family Planning Services: A Research Paper for the Special Study on Family Planning" (Washington: Office of Assistant Secretary for Planning and Evaluation, Department of Health, Education, and Welfare, Draft of March 14, 1969), p. iii. (Photocopied)

8. B. M. Mahajan, "Vasectomy Versus IUCD," Artha Vijñana (Poona), VIII, 2 (June 1966), 158.

9. Robert Repetto, "India: A Case Study of the Madras Vasectomy Program," Studies in Family Planning, 31 (May 1968), pp. 10-11.

10. A similar procedure is discussed in Roland N. McKean, Efficiency in Government Through Systems Analysis (New York: John Wiley and Sons, 1958), 93-95.

11. Repetto, "India: A Case Study," pp. 11-13.

12. Ibid., pp. 13-15.

13. Stephen Enke, "The Economic Aspects of Slowing Population Growth," The Economic Journal, LXXVI (March 1966), p. 50.

14. S. M. Keeny et al., "Korea and Taiwan: The Record for 1967," Studies in Family Planning, 29 (April 1968), pp. 1-9.

15. Ibid., p. 2.

16. Mahajan, "Vasectomy Versus IUCD," p. 157.

17. Ibid., p. 158.

18. George Zaidan, "Benefits and Costs of Population Control with Special Reference to the U.A.R. (Egypt)" (unpublished Ph.D. dissertation, Dept. of Economics, Harvard University, 1967).

19. Ibid., pp. 89-90.

20. John A. Ross, "Cost of Family Planning Programs," in Bernard Berelson et al, Family Planning and Population Programs, (Chicago: The University of Chicago Press, 1966), pp. 759-78.

21. Ibid., p. 777.

22. Seidman, Costs and Effectiveness, p. iii.

23. Ibid., pp. 34, 48-49, and 86-90.

24. Ibid., p. 85.

25. Zaidan, for example, assumes that a building of a certain size can serve 4-5,000 women per year and that there are no economies of scale. Zaidan, "Benefits and Costs of Population Control," pp. 101-10.

26. See, for example, the studies by Keeny, Mahajan, and Zaidan.

27. Seidman, "Benefits and Costs of Population Control," pp. 27, 48, and 49.

28. See, for example, Charles J. Hitch and Roland N. McKean, The Economics of Defense in the Nuclear Age (New York: Atheneum, 1967), pp. 168-69, or any of the Studies in Robert Dorfman, ed., Measuring Benefits of Government Investments (Washington: The Brookings Institution, 1965).

CHAPTER 2

1. G. Hadley, Linear Algebra (Reading, Mass.: Addison-Wesley Publishing, 1961), p. 195.

CHAPTER 3

1. Mindel C. Sheps and Edward B. Perrin, "Changes in Birth Rates as a Function of Contraceptive Effectiveness: Some Applications of a Stochastic Model," American Journal of Public Health and the Nation's Health, LIII, 7 (July 1963), 1031-46.

2. Ibid.

3. Ibid., p 1037.

4. Ibid.

5. See, for example, J. MacLeod et al., "In Vitro Assessment of Commercial Contraceptive Jellies and Creams," Journal of the American Medical Association, CLXXVI (May 6, 1961), pp. 427-31.

6. W. Parker Mauldin et al., "Retention of IUD's: An International Comparison," Studies in Family Planning, 18 (April 1967), pp. 5-6.

7. Philip C. Sagi et al., "Contraceptive Effectiveness as a Function of Desired Family Size," Population Studies, XV, 3 (March 1962), pp. 291-96.

8. Christopher Tietze, "The Clinical Effectiveness of Contraceptive Methods," American Journal of Obstetrics and Gynecology, LXXVIII, 3 (September 1959), pp. 650-56.

9. Hans Lehfeldt, "Willful Exposure to Unwanted Pregnancy (WEUP): Psychological Explanation for Patient Failure in Contraception," American Journal of Obstetrics and Gynecology, LXXVIII, 3 (September 1959), pp. 661-65.

10. M.-Francoise Hall and William A. Reinke, "Factors Influencing Contraceptive Continuation Rates: The Oral and Intrauterine Methods," Demography, VI, 3 (August 1969), p. 335.

11. Gavin W. Jones and W. Parker Mauldin, "Use of Oral Contraceptives: With Special Reference to Developing Countries," Studies in Family Planning, 24 (December 1967), p. 4.

12. Mauldin et al., "Retention of IUD's," p. 4.

13. Ibid., pp. 7-8; and Gerald Zatuchni, "International Postpartum Family Planning program: Report on the first year," Studies in Family Planning, 22 (August 1967), p. 22.

14. Hall and Reinke, "Contraceptive Continuation Rates," p. 342. This is probably evidence of a filtering process that tends to continuously remove the less motivated users.

15. Mauldin, "Births Averted by a Family Planning Program," in Clyde V. Kisner ed., Research in Family Planning (Princeton, N.J.: Princeton University Press, 1962), pp. 1-2.

16. Ibid., pp. 3-4.

17. Ibid.

18. Some of these problems are discussed in Robert G. Potter, Jr., "Length of the Observation Period as a Factor Affecting the Contraceptive Failure Rate," Milbank Memorial Fund Quarterly, XXXVIII, 2 (April 1960), pp. 140-52.

19. Robert G. Potter, Jr., "Estimating Births Averted in a Family Planning Program," in S. J. Behrman et al., Fertility and Family Planning: A World View (Ann Arbor, Michigan: The University of Michigan Press, 1969), p. 417.

20. Ibid., p. 418.

21. Ibid., p. 421.

22. U.S., Dept. of Health, Education, and Welfare, Public Health Service, Vital Statistics of the United States: 1967, Vol. I, Table I-12.

CHAPTER 4

1. Preston E. James, Latin America (3rd ed.; New York: The Odyssey Press, 1959), Chapter 30.

2. Ibid.

3. Ibid., pp. 792-93; Millard Hansen, "Puerto Rico," Collier's Encyclopedia, XIX (1967), p. 501.

4. James, Latin America, p. 793.

5. Antonio Hernandez Torres, "Puerto Rico's Profile" (San Juan: Department of Obstetrics and Gynecology, School of Medicine, University of Puerto Rico, May 1969), p. 2. (Mimeographed.)

6. Ibid., p. 1.

7. Puerto Rico, Oficina del Gobernador, Junta de Planificación, Informe Economico al Gobernador: 1970, p. A-23.

8. Ibid.

9. Ibid.

10. Calculated from data of U.S. Department of Commerce, quoted in U.S., President, Economic Report of the President (Washington: U.S. Government Printing Office, 1971), pp. 214-15.

11. U.S. Department of Commerce data cited in Luman H. Long, ed., The World Almanac and Book of Facts, (1972 ed.; New York: Newspaper Enterprise Association, 1971), p. 76.

12. Informe Economico, p. A-9.

13. Ibid., p. A-17.

14. Ibid., p. A-21.

15. The San Juan Star, June 27, 1969, p. 20.

16. Calculated from U.S. Office of Education data cited in Long, ed., The World Almanac, p. 331.

17. Hernandez Torres, "Puerto Rico's Profile," p. 4.

18. Ibid., p. 6.

19. James, Latin America p. 792; Estimate of the Population Reference Bureau, Inc., reported in El Mercado de Valores, XXXII, 6 (February 7, 1972), 126.

20. Dennis H. Wrong, Population and Society (2nd ed.; New York: Random House, 1961), pp. 17-23.

21. Celestina Zalduondo, "The Family Planning Program of Puerto Rico," (Rio Piedras, Puerto Rico: Family Planning Association of Puerto Rico), p. 1. (Mimeographed.)

22. U.S. Bureau of the Census, Census of Population: 1970. General Population Characteristics. Final Report PC(1)-B1 United States Summary, p. 1-263.

23. U.S. Census, pp. 1-263.

24. José L. Vázquez Calzada, "El Desbalance Entre Recursos Y Población en Puerto Rico," (San Juan: Demographic Section, School of Medicine, University of Puerto Rico, November, 1966), p. 8. (Mimeographed.)

25. Long, ed. The World Almanac, p. 157.

26. Ibid.

27. Vázquez Calzada, "El Desbalance Entre Recursos y Población," p. 13.

28. For recent empirical support for this point see Nathaniel H. Leff, "Dependency Rates and Savings Rates," The American Economic Review, LIX, 5 (December 1969), 886-96.

29. George W. Cadbury, "Outlook for Government Action in Family Planning in the West Indies," in Clyde V. Kiser, ed., Research in Family Planning (Princeton, N.J.: Princeton University Press, 1962), p. 320. Dagmar Schultz, "Poverty and Population: The Struggle in Puerto Rico," San Juan Review (October, 1966).

30. Zalduondo, "Family Planning Program," p. 2.

31. Schultz, "Poverty and Population."

32. Cadbury, "Outlook for Government Action," p. 320 (Schultz says there were 67 clinics).

33. Zalduondo, "Family Planning Program," p. 2.

34. Hernandez Torres, "Puerto Rico's Profile," p. 13.

35. Cadbury, "Outlook for Government Action," p. 320.

36. Zalduondo, "Family Planning Program" Schultz, "Poverty and Population."

37. Cadbury, "Outlook for Government Action," p. 320.

38. Schultz, "Poverty and Population."

39. Cadbury, "Outlook for Government Action," p. 321.

40. Reprinted in Zalduondo, "Family Planning Program," p. 5.

41. Policy statement of October, 1963 as reprinted in Zalduondo, "Family Planning Program," p. 7.

42. Ibid., p. 9.

CHAPTER 5

1. Most of the information in the next six paragraphs was obtained from Dr. Antonio Hernandez Torres in a personal interview on April 21, 1969.

2. Antonio Hernandez Torres, "Proposal for the Creation of an Island-Wide Program on Education, Service and Investigation to Improve Knowledge, Attitudes and Practice on Reproductive Physiology" (San Juan: Northeast Health Region, Puerto Rico Department of Health, February 1969), p. 37. (Mimeographed.)

3. This concept is discussed in A. A. Walters, "Production and Cost Functions: An Econometric Survey," Econometrica, XXXI (January-April, 1963), p. 12.

4. This opinion was expressed by Dr. Antonio Hernandèz Torres on several occasions.

5. Harvey Leibenstein, "The Proportionality Controversy and the Theory of Production," Quarterly Journal of Economics, LXIX (November 1955), p. 624.

6. Edward H. Chamberlin, "Proportionality, Divisibility, and Economies of Scale," Quarterly Journal of Economics, LXII (February 1948), p. 236.

7. Martin S. Feldstein, Economic Analysis for Health Service Efficiency (Chicago: Markham Publishing, 1968), pp. 115-20.

8. Interview with Dr. Antonio Hernandez Torres, April 21, 1969.

9. Puerto Rico, Oficina de Personal, División de Clasificación y Retribución, Estudio de Sueldos: 1968, pp. 6-7.

10. Puerto Rico, Oficina del Gobernador, Junta de Planificación, Informe Economico al Gobernador: 1970, p. A-23.

11. Personal interview with Sr. Jaime Camuñas, Assistant Regional Administrator, Northeast Health Region of Puerto Rico on July 30, 1969.

12. Hernandez Torres, "Proposal," p. 69.

13. Ibid.

14. The derivation of this estimate is outlined in the Appendix.

15. Hernandez Torres, "Proposal," pp. 71-72.

16. Hernandez Torres, "Proposal," p. 46.

17. Ibid., pp. 44-46.

18. Ibid.

19. Ibid.

20. This might happen if high fertility patients preferred a particular method or were encouraged by program personnel to select a particular method. This has been observed in Korea. See S. M. Keeny et al., "Korea and Taiwan: The Record for 1967," Studies in Family Planning, 29 (April 1968) 4.

21. J. Johnston, Econometric Methods (New York: McGraw-Hill, 1963), pp. 129-30.

22. A unified discussion of the problem of estimating contraceptive continuation functions, including the results for Humacao, appeared earlier in William J. Kelly, "Estimation of Contraceptive Continuation Functions," Demography, VIII, 3 (August 1971), 335-39. For additional evidence, see Peng-Tu Liu et al., "A Study On IUD Retention by Curve-Fitting," Demography, IX, 1 (February 1972), 1-11.

23. The test procedure is outlined in John E. Freund, Mathematical Statistics (Englewood Cliffs, N. J.: Prentice-Hall, 1962), pp. 290-92.

24. Milton Friedman, "The Methodology of Positive Economics" in William Breit and Harold M. Hochman, eds., Readings in Microeconomics (New York: Holt, Rinehart and Winston, 1968), p. 46.

25. The procedure followed is outlined in Freund, Mathematical Statistics, pp. 285-89.

26. Lower rates are to be expected in the second year because the most fertile women tend to become pregnant first. See Mindel C. Sheps, "Report on the Panel Discussion" in M. C. Sheps and J. C. Ridley, eds., Public Health and Population Change (Pittsburgh: University of Pittsburgh Press, 1965), pp. 494-98.

27. Celso-Ramon Garcia and Gregory Pincus, "Ovulation Inhibition by Progestin-estrogen Combination," International Journal of Fertility, IX, 1 (January-March, 1964), 96.

28. The cost figures derived here represent the minimum levels of marginal costs of preventing a birth, i.e., the costs for the situation where output needs are known exactly and hence inputs need not be in excess. Once queuing is allowed, expected marginal costs will be greater than these figures and can rise to any level depending on the degree of overcapacity that is permitted.

29. A more detailed discussion of the problem of estimating the number of births prevented appeared earlier in William J. Kelly, "Estimation of Births Averted by Family Planning Programs: The Parity Approach," Studies in Family Planning, II, 9 (September 1971), 197-201.

30. Interview with Sr. Gonzalez, Depto. de Finanzas, Corporación de Servicio del Centro Medico de Puerto Rico, July 18, 1969.

31. These are the author's estimates, based on indicative information supplied by the Upjohn Company. It is here assumed that the contraceptive is purchased in moderate quantities. The actual costs would vary from these figures depending on purchase volume, shipping costs, and import duties. It is estimated, for example, that the 3 month form would cost approximately $.65 per dose if purchased and shipped in very large quantities. Telephone interview with Thomas J. Vecchio, Upjohn International, Inc., May 12, 1970.

32. Ibid.

33. Stephen Enke, "The Economic Aspects of Slowing Population Growth," The Economic Journal, LXXVI (March 1966), 47. It is interesting to note that this figure falls within the range suggested by Earnhardt's partial study of the value of a birth prevented in Puerto Rico ($2,528-4,126). See Chapter 4.

CHAPTER 6

1. This figure was supplied by the staff of the Postpartum, Cytology, and Family Planning Program.

2. For evidence on the effect of waiting time on the continuation rate see Alan Keller, "Mexico City: A Clinic Dropout Study," Studies in Family Planning, II, 9 (September, 1971), 196, Table 4.

3. See, for example, George P. Cernada, "Direct Mailings to Promote Family Planning," Studies in Family Planning, 53 (May, 1970), 16-19.

4. See Hernandez Torres, "Proposal," pp. 65-72.

5. The reader interested in pursuing this topic might begin by investigating the economic and social consequences of other great demographic changes. See, for example, John Saltmarsh, "Plague and Economic Decline in England in the Later Middle Ages" in Warren C. Scoville and J. Clayburn La Force, eds., The Middle Ages and the Renaissance (Lexington, Mass.: D.C. Heath and Company, 1969).

PUBLIC DOCUMENTS

Puerto Rico. ,Departamento de Salud, División de Registro Demográfico y Estadísticas Vitales. Informe Anual de Estadísticas Vitales: 1968. Departamento de Salud, 1968.

Puerto Rico. Oficina del Gobernador, Junta de Planificación. Informe Economico al Gobernador: 1970. Oficina del Gobernador, 1970.

Puerto Rico. Oficina de Personal, División de Clasificación y Retribución. Estudio de Sueldos: 1968. Oficina de Personal, 1968.

U.S. Department of Health, Education, and Welfare, Public Health Service. Vital Statistics of the United States: 1967. Vol. I. Washington, D.C.: The Department, 1967.

U.S. President. Economic Report of the President. Washington, D.C.: U.S. Government Printing Office, 1971.

BOOKS

Berelson, Bernard, et al. Family Planning and Population Programs. Chicago: The University of Chicago Press, 1966.

Coale, Ansley J. and Edgar M. Hoover. Population Growth and Economic Development in Low-Income Countries. Princeton, N.J.: Princeton University Press, 1958.

Dorfman, Robert, ed. Measuring Benefits of Government Investments. Washington, D.C.: The Brookings Institution, 1965.

Eastman, N. J. and L. M. Hellman. Williams' Obstetrics. 13th ed. New York: Appleton-Century-Crofts, 1966.

Feldstein, Martin S. Economic Analysis for Health Service Efficiency. Chicago: Markham Publishing, 1968.

Freund, John E. Mathematical Statistics. Englewood Cliffs, N.J.: Prentice-Hall, 1962.

Golenpaul, Dan, ed. Information Please Almanac, Atlas and Yearbook. 1964 ed. New York: Simon and Schuster, 1963.

Hadley, G. Linear Algebra. Reading, Mass.: Addison-Wesley Publishing 1961.

Hitch, Charles J. and Roland N. McKean. The Economics of Defense in the Nuclear Age. New York: Atheneum, 1967.

James, Preston E. Latin America. 3rd ed. New York: The Odyssey Press, 1959.

Johnston, J. Econometric Methods. New York: McGraw-Hill Book Company, 1963.

_____ Statistical Cost Analysis. New York: McGraw-Hill Book Company, 1960.

Long, Luman H., ed. The World Almanac and Book of Facts. 1972 ed., New York: Newspaper Enterprise Association, 1971.

McKean, Roland N. Efficiency in Government Through Systems Analysis. New York: John Wiley and Sons, 1958.

Ohlin, Goran. Population Control and Economic Development. Paris: The Organisation for Economic Co-operation and Development, 1967.

Smith, Vernon L. Investment and Production. Cambridge, Mass.: Harvard University Press, 1961.

When More is Less. New York: Planned Parenthood Federation of America, 1968.

Wrong, Dennis H. Population and Society. 2d ed. New York: Random House, 1961.

ARTICLES AND PERIODICALS

Agarwala, S. N. "Evaluating the Effectiveness of a Family Planning Program," Research in Family Planning. Edited by Clyde V. Kiser. Princeton, N.J.: Princeton University Press, 1962. pp. 409-420.

Alchian, Armen. "Costs and Output," The Allocation of Economic
    Resources. Moses Abramovitz et al. Stanford, Calif.: Stanford
    University Press, 1959. Pp. 23-40.

Barten, A. P. "Note on Unbiased Estimation of the Squared Multiple
    Correlation Coefficient," Statistica Neerlandica, XVI, 2 (1962),
    151-63.

Besen, Stanley M., et al. "Cost-Effectiveness Analysis for the 'War
    on Poverty'." Cost-Effectiveness Analysis. Edited by Thomas
    A. Goldman. New York: Frederick A. Praeger, Publishers,
    1967. Pp. 140-54.

Cadbury, George W. "Outlook for Government Action in Family
    Planning in the West Indies," Research in Family Planning.
    Edited by Clyde V. Kiser. Princeton, N.J.: Princeton University
    Press, 1962. Pp. 317-33.

Calderone, Mary S. "An Inventory of Contraceptive Methods Adapted
    to Public Health Practice," American Journal of Public Health
    and the Nation's Health, LII, 10 (October 1962), 1712-19.

Carter, Luther J. "Population Control: U.S. Aid Program Leaps
    Forward," Science, CLIX (February 9, 1968), 611-14.

Cernada, George P. "Direct Mailings to Promote Family Planning,"
    Studies in Family Planning, 53 (May 1970), 16-19.

Chamberlin, Edward H. "Proportionality, Divisibility, and Economies
    of Scale," Quarterly Journal of Economics, LXII (February 1948),
    229-62.

Cooper, W. W., and A. Charnes. "Silhouette Functions of Short Run
    Cost Behavior," Quarterly Journal of Economics, LXVIII, 1
    (February 1954), 131-50.

Daly, Herman E. "The Population Question in Northeast Brazil: Its
    Economic and Ideological Dimensions," Economic Development
    and Cultural Change, XVIII, 4, Part I (July 1970), 536-74.

Enke, Stephen. "The Economic Aspects of Slowing Population Growth,"
    The Economic Journal, LXXVI, 301 (March 1966), 44-56.

Friedman, Milton. "The Methodology of Positive Economics,"
    Readings in Microeconomics. Edited by William Breit and

Harold M. Hochman. New York: Holt, Rinehart and Winston, 1968. Pp. 23-47.

Garcia, Celso-Ramon, and Gregory Pincus. "Ovulation Inhibition by Progestin-estrogen Combination," International Journal of Fertility, IX, 1 (January-March 1964), 95-105.

Hall, M.-Françoise, and William A. Reinke. "Factors Influencing Contraceptive Continuation Rates: The Oral and Intrauterine Methods," Demography, VI, 3 (August 1969), 335-46.

Hansen, Millard. "Puerto Rico," Colliers Encyclopedia, XIX (1967). Pp. 499-508.

Hellman, Louis M., et al. "United States Food and Drug Administration: Report on Intrauterine Devices by the Advisory Committee on Obstetrics and Gynecology," Studies in Family Planning, 27 (March 1968), 12-15.

"India: A Bleak Demographic Future," Population Bulletin, XXVI, 5 (November 1970), 2-12.

Jones, Gavin W., and W. Parker Mauldin. "Use of Oral Contraceptives: With Special Reference to Developing Countries," Studies in Family Planning, 24 (December 1967), 1-13.

Kantner, John F. "The Place of Conventional Methods in Family Planning Programs," Family Planning and Population Programs. Bernard Berelson et al. Chicago: The University of Chicago Press, 1966. Pp. 403-10.

Keeny, S. M., et al. "Korea and Taiwan: The Record for 1967," Studies in Family Planning, 29 (April 1968), 1-9.

Keller, Alan. "Mexico City: A Clinic Dropout Study," Studies in Family Planning, II, 9 (September 1971), 192-96.

Kelly, William J. "Estimation of Births Averted by Family Planning Programs: The Parity Approach," Studies in Family Planning, II, 9 (September 1971), 197-201.

_____. "Estimation of Contraceptive Continuation Functions," Demography, VIII, 3 (August 1971), 335-39.

Leff, Nathaniel H. "Dependency Rates and Savings Rates," The American Economic Review, LIX, 5 (December 1969), 886-96.

Lehfeldt, Hans. "Willful Exposure to Unwanted Pregnancy (WEUP): Psychological Explanation for Patient Failure in Contraception," American Journal of Obstetrics and Gynecology, LXXVIII, 3 (September 1959), 661-65.

Leibenstein, Harvey. "The Proportionality Controversy and the Theory of Production," Quarterly Journal of Economics, LXIX (November 1955), 619-25.

Levin, Harry L. "Distribution of Contraceptive Supplies Through Commercial Channels," Family Planning and Population Programs. Bernard Berelson et al. Chicago: The University of Chicago Press, 1966. Pp. 487-94.

Liu, Peng-Tu, et al. "A Study on IUD Retention by Curve-Fitting," Demography, IX, 1 (February 1972), 1-11.

MacLeod, J., et al. "In Vitro Assessment of Commercial Contraceptive Jellies and Creams," Journal of the American Medical Association, CLXXVI (May 6, 1961), 427-31.

Mahajan, B. M. "Vasectomy Versus IUCD," Artha Vijñana (Poona), VIII, 2 (June 1966), 149-60.

Mauldin, W. Parker. "Births Averted by Family Planning Programs," Studies in Family Planning, 33 (August 1968), 1-7.

Mauldin, W. Parker, et al. "Retention of IUD's: An International Comparison," Studies in Family Planning, 18 (April 1967), 1-12.

Medical Research Council. "Risk of Thromboembolic Disease in Women Taking Oral Contraceptives: A Preliminary Communication to the Medical Research Council by a Subcommittee," The British Medical Journal, 5548 (May 6, 1967), 355-59.

Muramatsu, Minoru. "Japan: Miracle in East Asia," Family-Planning Programs: An International Survey. Edited by Bernard Berelson. New York: Basic Books, 1969. Pp. 15-25.

Myint, Hla. "The 'Classical Theory' of International Trade and the Underdeveloped Countries," Economics of Trade and Development. Edited by James D. Theberge. New York: John Wiley and Sons, 1968. Pp. 188-210.

Population Reference Bureau. "1971 World Population Data Sheet." Washington: Population Reference Bureau, 1971.

Potter, Robert G., Jr. "Estimating Births Averted in a Family Planning Program," Fertility and Family Planning: A World View. Edited by S. J. Behrman et al. Ann Arbor, Michigan: The University of Michigan Press, 1969. Pp. 413-34.

_____ "Length of the Observation Period as a Factor Affecting the Contraceptive Failure Rate," Milbank Memorial Fund Quarterly, XXXVIII, 2 (April 1960), 140-52.

Prest, A. R., and R. Turvey. "Cost-Benefit Analysis: A Survey," Economic Journal, LXXV, 300 (December 1965), 683-735.

Repetto, Robert. "India: A Case Study of the Madras Vasectomy Program," Studies in Family Planning, 31 (May 1968), 8-16.

Rice-Wray, Edris. "The Provoked Abortion—A Major Public Health Problem," American Journal of Public Health and the Nation's Health, LIV, 2 (February 1964), 313-21.

Rodgers, David A., et al. "A Longitudinal Study of the Psycho-Social Effects of Vasectomy," Journal of Marriage and the Family, XXVII, 1 (February 1965), 59-64.

Ross, John A. "Cost of Family Planning Programs," Family Planning and Population Programs. Bernard Berelson et al. Chicago: The University of Chicago Press, 1966. Pp. 759-78.

Sagi, Philip C., et al. "Contraceptive Effectiveness as a Function of Desired Family Size," Population Studies, XV, 3 (March 1962), 291-96.

Saltmarsh, John. "Plague and Economic Decline in England in the Later Middle Ages," The Middle Ages and the Renaissance. Edited by Warren C. Scoville and J. Clayburn La Force. Lexington, Mass.: D. C. Heath and Company, 1969. Pp. 111-29.

Samuel. T. J. "Allocation and Utilization of Resources for Population Control in India," Indian Journal of Economics (Allahabad), XLVI, 182 (January 1966), 245-62.

The San Juan Star. (June 27, 1969).

Saunders, Lyle. "Research and Evaluation: Needs for the Future,"
Family Planning and Population Programs. Bernard Berelson
et al. Chicago: The University of Chicago Press, 1966. Pp.
779-88.

Schultz, Dagmar. "Poverty and Population: The Struggle in Puerto
Rico," San Juan Review (October 1966).

Sheps, Mindel C. "Report on the Panel Discussion," Public Health
and Population Change. Edited by M. C. Sheps and J. C. Ridley.
Pittsburgh: University of Pittsburgh Press, 1965. Pp. 487-98.

Sheps, Mindel C. and Edward B Perrin. "Changes in Birth Rates as
a Function of Contraceptive Effectiveness: Some Applications
of a Stochastic Model," American Journal of Public Health and
the Nation's Health, LIII, 7 (July 1963), 1031-46.

Simon, Julian L. "The Role of Bonuses and Persuasive Propaganda in
the Reduction of Birth Rates," Economic Development and
Cultural Change, XVI, 3 (April 1968), 404-11.

Tietze, Christopher. "The Clinical Effectiveness of Contraceptive
Methods," American Journal of Obstetrics and Gynecology,
LXXVIII, 3 (September 1959), 650-56.

_____ "The Effect of Breast Feeding on the Rate of Conception,"
International Population Conference: New York, 1961, II (1963)
129-36.

Viel, Benjamin. "The Social Consequences of Population Growth,"
PRB Selection No. 30 (1969), 1-6.

Vinod, H. D. "Econometrics of Joint Production," Econometrica,
XXXVI, 2 (April 1968), 322-36.

Walters, A. A. "Production and Cost Functions: An Econometric
Survey," Econometrica, XXXI (January-April 1963), 1-66.

Weintraub, Robert. "The Birth Rate and Economic Development: An
Empirical Study," Econometrica, XL, 4 (October 1962), 812-17.

Zatuchni, Gerald. "International Postpartum Family Planning Program:
Report on the First Year," Studies in Family Planning, 22
(August 1967), 1-23.

UNPUBLISHED MATERIALS

"Conceptual and Methodological Problems Connected with Cost-Ef-
    fectiveness Studies of Family Planning Programs." Mimeographed.
    Working Paper No. 1 of Penn State—U.S. AID Population Control
    Project, Department of Economics, Pennsylvania State University,
    1968.

Earnhardt, Kent Cline. "Population Growth and Educational Investment
    in Puerto Rico, 1970-1990." Unpublished Master's dissertation,
    Graduate Program in Planning, University of Puerto Rico, 1968.

Hernandez Torres, Antonio. "Puerto Rico's Profile." Mimeographed.
    San Juan: Department of Obstetrics and Gynecology, School of
    Medicine, University of Puerto Rico, May 1969.

_____. "Proposal for the Creation of an Island-Wide Program on
    Education, Service and Investigation to Improve Knowledge,
    Attitudes and Practice on Reproductive Physiology." Mimeo-
    graphed. San Juan: Northeast Health Region, Puerto Rico
    Department of Health, February 1969.

Horlocher, David E. "Measuring the Economic Benefits of Population
    Control: A Critical Review of the Literature." Mimeographed.
    Working Paper No. 2 of Penn State—U.S. AID Population Control
    Project, Department of Economics, Pennsylvania State University,
    1968.

Robinson, Warren C. "Cost-Benefit Analysis and the Evaluation of
    Population Control Programs." Mimeographed. Department
    of Economics, Pennsylvania State University, 1967.

Seidman, David R. "Costs and Effectiveness of Alternative Modes of
    Delivering Family Planning Services: A Research Paper for
    the Special Study on Family Planning." Photocopied. Washington:
    Office of Assistant Secretary for Planning and Evaluation,
    Department of Health, Education, and Welfare draft of March
    14, 1969.

Vázquez Calzada, José L. "El Desbalance Entre Recursos y
    Población en Puerto Rico." Mimeographed. San Juan: Demo-
    graphic Section, School of Medicine, University of Puerto Rico,
    November, 1966.

Zaidan, George. "Benefits and Costs of Population Control with Special Reference to the U.A.R. (Egypt)." Unpublished Ph.D. dissertation, Department of Economics, Harvard University, 1967.

Zalduondo, Celestina. "The Family Planning Program of Puerto Rico." Mimeographed. Rio Piedras, Puerto Rico: Family Planning Association of Puerto Rico.

PERSONAL INTERVIEWS
AND CORRESPONDENCE

Agency for International Development. Personal interview with Dr. Harold Frederiksen of the Population Service. July 2, 1968.

Office of the Assistant Secretary (Planning and Evaluation), U.S. Department of Health, Education, and Welfare. Personal interviews with Dr. Phillip Corfman, Dr. Richard H. Seder, and Dr. David R. Seidman. July 2, 1968.

Planned Parenthood of Houston. Personal interviews with Norman Fleishman, Executive Director. April, 1968; February, 1969.

Puerto Rico. Corporación de Servicio del Centro Medico de Puerto Rico, Rio Piedras, Puerto Rico. Personal interview with Sr. Gonzalez, Departamento de Finanzas. July 18, 1969.

Puerto Rico. Health Department. Personal interviews with Sr. Jaime Camuñas, Assistant Regional Administrator, and other personnel of the Northeast Health Region of Puerto Rico. July, 1969.

Puerto Rico. University of Puerto Rico, School of Medicine. Personal interviews with Antonio Hernandez Torres, M.D., and other personnel of the Oficina Post-Parto, Citología, y Métodos. April-August, 1969.

Upjohn International, Inc. Correspondence and telephone conversations with Thomas J. Vecchio, M.D. May, 1970.

ABOUT THE AUTHOR

WILLIAM J. KELLY is a faculty member of the Department of Economics and Statistics of the University of Georgia. Dr. Kelly received a B.A. degree (magna cum laude) from the University of Massachusetts and his M.A. and Ph.D. degrees in economics from Rice University. He has also pursued studies at Pennsylvania State University, the University of Richmond, and Bowdoin College, where he was named a James Bowdoin Scholar in 1961. In addition to his academic career he has worked for the Fibers Division of Allied Chemical Corporation, McGraw-Hill Book Company, the Library of Congress, and the Woods Hole Oceanographic Institute, and has testified before the Massachusetts House of Representatives on population growth.

Dr. Kelly, who speaks Russian, French, and Spanish, teaches development economics, labor economics, comparative economic systems, and European economic history. He is at present pursuing research on the economics of population and population control, particularly with respect to less developed countries.